HEAR YOUR BODY
WHISPER

HOW TO UNLOCK YOUR
SELF-HEALING MECHANISM

OTAKARA KLETTKE

As my thanks to you for buying this book, I am giving you a free download of a meditation to do in the evening at

https://otakaraklettke.com/meditation

Record it with your own voice, adjust it to your needs and play it for yourself.

Disclaimer

The information in this book is based on the author's own experience and research.

It is the reader's own responsibility to consult a physician or therapist before using information provided in this book especially in regards to one's health symptoms that may require proper diagnosis or professional medical attention.

ACKNOWLEDGMENTS

There were many people who supported me
on the journey of writing this book.

Thank you all from the bottom of my heart for helping me to
write and continually improve this book.

Special thanks to my editor Denice Hughes Lewis who has
never-ending patience,
Nickole Harris for being way more than a beta reader,
Jaromira Valeckova and Oskar Stastny for the beautiful book
cover,
Marissa Tims, Al Davis and Andy Dill for being there with me
at the right time,
All folks from SPS community: I owe you more than the
words of a writer could ever say!
And of course all of you in my launch team were spectacular!

DEDICATION

I would like to dedicate this book to your amazing body and you, the reader.

If you weren't here this book wouldn't have a purpose.

Thank you.

Table of Contents

Introduction

The Secret

"Natural forces within us are the true healers of disease."

Hippocrates

I wanted to die. I was 16 years old and hurt so much that I prayed to be free from the pain. It happened after surgery on my ovary. My malfunctioning liver gave out. There was nothing I could do.

I saw only yellow light. My blood was so bad, I went temporarily blind, vomited constantly, and couldn't sit up. Every wave of regurgitation pulled on my freshly cut stomach muscles and organs. Acid burned my throat where tubes from the surgery had agitated it. Because I wasn't able to move as I normally would after surgery, some of my organs grew together.

My ill health started when I was just a baby. I was sick most of my childhood. There were years I missed over 80% of school. Every year it seemed that I faced some new health issue. I wasn't allowed to do PE classes, carry my schoolbooks, or do anything that would tire me.

Today I love my body with every flaw that it has. And my body loves me! I rarely ever catch a cold. The issues that the doctors insisted and believed I would have forever; gone.

I feel I am at a healthy body weight. I love all I eat. Most days, I love to exercise. Besides my pregnancy and giving birth to my daughter, I have sought a doctor's help twice in the past 15 years.

Over the years I found an amazing connection between my body and my mind. I believe that what I do is replicable and anyone can achieve the results that I did. I consider my mind to be living in a symbiotic relationship with my body. One can not survive without the other. I treat my body as a different entity from my mind.

It's taken me about 25 years to slowly refine the process that I am offering you. I will not tell you if you should eat breakfast or take cycling classes. You will find the answers if you listen to the way your body talks. I will teach you the language and how to create a real relationship and connection with your body.

The hard times of my life turned me into an avid reader and researcher. They allowed me to find solutions and to share them with you now.

Do you ever wonder what your life would be like if you had the body of your dreams without stressing over it? To be healthy and at your ideal body weight? Not having to suffer through exercise you don't like or being on the diet that you can't wait to end?

The human body is absolutely amazing. It can self-heal almost any sickness and stay at a happy body weight. It can even tell you how to get there.

Your body has been programmed for millions of years. Now you need to connect with it to become aware of what it needs.You will learn that communicating is an easy process. You will know and crave food that is best for your body, which exercise or diet is ideal, and joyful for you, and how to stay healthy during times when you don't have a chance to be your body's best buddy.

Since you are reading this book, the chances are that you are unhappy in some way with your body. If that's true, take a moment and ask this important question. Why? Why I am not in the shape I wish?

Unless your answer has to do with some major injury, I think that your body-mind connection isn't working to its potential. Doctors and scientists claim that 90% of all diseases are caused by stress, therefore by your mind. What you eat does matter and your body does require some movement, but you will be surprised how little your body really needs when given proper attention.

The weight-loss and drug industries are some of the highest profitable businesses in the world for one main reason. Their solutions rarely work for the problems. People who don't find help come back to try another diet next year, another miracle pill, or hope to stick with a new kind of exercise program. There is a small chance that they will succeed. These industries are well aware of it.

After I healed most of my problems, I worked as a personal trainer for a large gym. I put people on a diet generated by a computer. The diet was based on people's food preferences. It sounded very 'personal' but was far from it.

The whole system was based on the idea that with exercise and less calorie input than output per day, you will have your ideal body. I had a hard time putting people through that. I knew that the results would come only if my clients had enough willpower.

I placed people on a program that was designed to put them in a battle with their own bodies, something most weight-loss programs do. Even if the results came, they were not lasting. Maybe the mind won the battle, but had no chance of winning the war.

Just as you cannot control your breathing or your digestion, you cannot boss your body around. The only way to win is to become friends with your body. You have to care enough to gain your body's trust in order for it to work with you.

The solution is quite simple. Befriend your body. Get rid of the toxins stored inside and become your own best friend. From that moment on, you can have the body that you will be happy with forever. I am quite sure that if your mind and body are in harmony, you don't need this book.

You will learn to tune into your body and communicate with it. The mutual balance will empower you. Even if there is stress in your life, you can keep your body healthy and fit. In return, your body will lessen the negative impact of stress and allow you to handle it in a healthier manner. You will understand what is best for you. When this happens your body will turn into the self-healing machine it is meant to be. You will create your own simple way to stay healthy and have all the tools to make the right decisions.

When it comes to food, most people crave what sounds good or what they love to eat regardless of whether or not their body wants it. The moment you give a green light to your body cravings instead of your mind cravings, everything changes. You want what is best for you. No willpower is needed. No struggle ensues. The body balances and heals itself.

There is one important ingredient that allows this process to work. You have to discover how to love yourself in the purest form.

Self-love is almost a rebellious act in today's society. On one hand, you hear that it is important to be yourself and to love who you are. On the other hand, you hear about not being selfish or vain. It is far more acceptable to complain to your friends about the tires around your stomach or the cold that has repeated for the fourth time this season than to say, "My body is so awesome! I wouldn't change a thing even if I could." Or, "I caught a virus, but my body is fighting like a rock star."

You do not love yourself when you are selfish. The emotion of selfishness is based on fear: of having less than others, of being judged, of being unattractive. Any fear-based emotion is the opposite of true love energy.

I am talking about love without condition. Love that understands that your body is doing the best it can for you despite your mind. It is doing the best it can even if it is obese or has a chronic disease. It certainly doesn't deserve your mind's criticism. The moment you understand this concept, it can be as if a light bulb turns on inside you.

Give yourself a big hug. Close your eyes, sink your mind inside yourself and let your body know that you are about to embark on an exciting journey.

Chapter 1

Every Body is Individual

"It is a shame for a man to grow old without ever seeing the strength and beauty of which his body is capable."

Socrates

Your body is amazing. Even if you may not think so, I do. I know that no matter what your circumstances, at this very moment you are alive because of your body.

You are meant to live in harmony with your body. It is the temple for your soul. You should celebrate it.

You can try to use your willpower to achieve a healthier or skinnier body. The truth is that your willpower, no matter how strong, can only push you so far and so long. Your subconscious mind will always win in the end.

You tend to forget about your body. I don't think you want to be cruel. The busy world and your life make you take your body for granted. Then the forgotten body gains weight, has no idea how to process certain food additives or compounds and develops health issues.

You cannot go into a war with your body and ever expect to win. Your body cannot lose. Your consciousness depends on residing in your live body.

Therefore, the only way to win is if you work together. The key is to help your body win and then you win.

Your body is unique. Study your body and celebrate what it can do for you. Your body's needs and wants may be totally different than what your spouse's needs are. It can be different from what well-meaning nutritionists or personal trainers think you need.

There are common differences and similarities within the human body. It is true that you can generally fit into a larger box that represents a good lifestyle. But the tight fit must be done just for you. There is no miracle life plan that is meant to fit everyone. No diet plan without a slight alteration is truly personal. You are special. Respect that.

Let's look at some general differences. Men and women have different needs for the kinds of foods and exercises they do.

Males tend to be more steak-and-potato kind of people, high on meat and low on vegetables. That's not necessarily a bad thing. Generally speaking, males also tend to exercise with heavy weights for short bursts of time unlike women who are much more cardio-oriented.

In evolutionary terms, human males hunted game that

required tracking and waiting patiently in silence. That also explains why men talk less than women. If the hunters were successful, they caught an animal. The catch often required additional work before the hunter could take it home. Hungry men ate some of the meat at the hunting grounds, thus eating more meat than women and children. Carrying the prey back required more physical effort if the prey was big. If the prey was small and men hunted in groups, no meat made it back to the camp.

Women were busy gathering food, preparing for winter, curing animal skins for clothing and bearing children. It was more natural for women to eat fruits and vegetables and to snack. They also moved throughout the day at a steady pace.

According to evolutionary anthropologists, children were in charge of other siblings. Interestingly, women raised their first offspring who then took care of the younger siblings or other kids in the neighborhood. Kids ate whatever was at home. Their turn came last.

Tastes change and evolve. You probably ate things as a child that you don't eat now. You learned to enjoy new flavors. How can you fit into a dietary category when you don't care for the bubblegum shaved ice you loved when you were five? During every stage of your life, your body needs something else. In every stage, the bacteria and other microorganisms on and in your body are slightly different and serve different purposes.

What about being a vegetarian, vegan or plain omnivore? Can anyone tell you that your choice isn't the right one? Not really. Being a vegetarian may be a perfectly fine option for one person, but can result in an iron or vitamin B12 deficiency in another.

I had been told my whole life that I must eat breakfast. I never liked it. I stopped eating breakfasts when I was in my late teens.

I rarely eat breakfasts to this day. My body isn't ready to start digesting that early. I start my day off with a small wake-up call--a cup of tea with milk and honey. But I don't eat solid food, sometimes not for hours.

This was one of the things that I discussed all the time with my fitness-enthusiastic friends. I was told by almost everyone that the way I ate would make me fat.

I only gained weight when I was fighting with my body. When I was doing that, I was actually eating less than normal. Despite what I was told or read in many books, I never got overweight by skipping my first meal of the day. I was also forced to tell people whom I trained the importance of eating breakfast.

My genetic pool suggests I should be overweight. All the females in my family are on the verge of being obese. Yet I don't have that problem. I exercise a little but not a lot. I eat mostly organic food. I often eat past midnight. I don't take any pills and as far as I know, my organs are pretty healthy. I don't see a doctor, other than a dentist. I leave my health to my extraordinary body. I am so grateful to have it.

Celebrate your body. Get in front of the mirror and just admire what you have, your own unique body.

You can and you should achieve whatever is within your body limits! You learned to acknowledge your unique mind and body as well as some evolutionary reasons for the difference between men's, women's and children's needs.

In the next chapter you will learn how to start turning your awareness inside your body and about the exciting army of helpers that are there to help you with every single cell. This army has ten times as many cells as your body has, so relax, you are being royally pampered.

Chapter 2

Building Awareness

*"Health of body and mind is a great blessing,
if we can bear it."*

John Henry Cardinal Newman

The human body is a beautiful, live machine run by bacteria, microorganisms, fungi and archaea (one of the first organisms on Earth). You have ten times more of these microscopic creature cells in your body than you have human cells. Of course, these cells are significantly smaller. That's why you have so many more. Overall they are somewhere between one to three percent of your body weight. If you weigh 150 pounds, you have approximately 1.5 to 4.5 pounds of microbes inside you.

What scientists know now is something new and very exciting.

In 2012, the Human Microbiome Project (HMP) Consortium, consisting of almost eighty universities and scientific institutions, brought to the world the largest map ever created of the human microbiome.

"Like fifteenth century explorers describing the outline of a new continent, HMP researchers employed a new technological strategy to define, for the first time, the normal microbial makeup of the human body," said NIH Director Francis S. Collins, M.D., PhD.

HMP reported that these primitive organisms contribute more genes to human survival than the human body does. For example, the bacteria in our gut are responsible for digesting food and extracting nutrients. Others produce compounds that regulate some of the immune system's response to disease. Most of these microbes know exactly what to do inside a healthy body. However, when the body's balance has shifted, problems can arise.

Because the organisms are far more primitive, your understanding needs to tune into their language. It's similar to listening and talking to a pet or a toddler. You understand the needs of your one-year-old when she tells you something in gibberish because it's your baby. You spend all the time with her. Others may not understand. It is the same thing when it comes to communicating with your body. You can listen to your body as no doctor, healer or shaman can.

I will talk about the inhabitants of your body more in Chapter Four.

I refer to the body throughout this book as a different entity from your mind and soul. Your body is home to your mind and soul and many other inhabitants. Even though you live inside, your body isn't really you. Let that idea sink in, at least while you read this book. Practice its concepts. Your mind is the leader and therefore most important, so relax. You are still in charge!

You have basic needs that are the same or very similar to everyone else's, but on the finite end, they are unique to you. You will learn to tune into your body and learn its language.

All language learning happens internally. Your awareness needs to be able to sink inside your body, as you will learn in Chapter Ten. As you practice this and as your body cleans itself from toxins, you will gain a better understanding.

Drugs can delay the process: prescription or nonprescription pills, sugars, caffeine, nicotine, alcohol or even worse. These substances change the behavior of your microorganisms. You still can communicate, but it's kind of like talking to a kid with Attention Deficient Disorder. I will talk about this more in detail in Chapter Five.

Do not stop using what you need or like. Don't stop eating chocolate if that is your thing. Don't quit smoking just yet. And never stop taking medication from your doctor without his consent.

Don't raise your eyebrow at me. You need your body healthy. And maybe you will give up all of the drugs or maybe some will be okay to keep. Some might be dangerous, but at this stage you need not worry about that. You need your body's trust. That doesn't happen by withholding something your body and mind are used to having.

Just observe yourself. I would suggest that you create

a notebook for that. Take your day and write down what your body does during the day.

When you wake up, how do you feel? Is it easy for you to get out of bed or are you tired? How long after you get up does your bowel movement engage? Do you eat breakfast? How long after you get up do you eat? Are you conscientiously hungry when you sit down to eat? What do you drink? Do you snack throughout the day? Are you hungry when you reach for that snack?

Observe your habits and always connect them with how your body and mind feel at that moment. Is the craving for ice cream due to hunger or is it your mind's craving?

Your observation doesn't have to be long term. A few normal days provide a good sample. Then if you have a special day, such as a holiday, write it in your journal as well. There are two rules: do not judge yourself and do not try to change yourself during this observation time.

It is important that you know what you tend to do. Without judgment. Be an observer. Do this exercise for a few days and stay mindful about it the whole time. It's all part of the process. To bring balance into your body you need to be aware about what is out of balance. Because our daily routine is often habitual, we aren't really aware of what we do. Never, and I mean never, get upset with your body.

Guilt is a sure block between you and your body. If you look at it from the body's perspective, you can understand why. It is usually your mind that decides to do something that is not good for the body. Then the mind generates guilt that the body is supposed to feel when it's not the body's fault!

This creates dis--ease in the body.
Enjoy all of your senses. Tastes and smells especially,

because these are your bridges into body awareness. When you eat, put all of your attention on taste. Slow down. Be present with your body. Don't let your mind fly into cyberspace.

Think about how food is going to be received in your stomach. Who is going to benefit from it? Be aware when you are no longer hungry. Are you the kind of a person who finishes your plate out of habit? Or maybe a busy mom who forgets to feed herself? Eating has become habitual behavior for many people.

At the time you eat, you often leave all the work for your body and microorganisms to deal with. While you have the power to give direction about how to utilize this meal, you simply disengage.

This is the time when the mind needs to lead and the body needs to follow its direction. In this book, you will learn how to do just that. The best part is that you don't have to do it all the time. Once you connect with your body and give direction for digestion, your body will continue to do that. Of course, you should check in every once in a while.

This is done to produce harmony and love toward your body. You don't need to follow any diet that would try to conform you into a mold. You will find out how to personalize what is best for you and what, how, or when to eat. The same is true about exercise. This is what creates the best potential for your body.

The cornerstone for your body connection is simply monitoring what you tend to do. It doesn't have to take longer than a couple of seconds at a time. For these couple of seconds, bring your full focus inside your body. Even if you get a sliver or are chronically tired, bring your conscious focus to the place of the body's suffering. Try to stay free of emotions. Work on being the ultimate observer. The best top managers are people that can lead many others and keep them happy and productive. They do it by being good and kind listeners as well as firm and egoless leaders.

In the next chapter, you are going to have a look at the place where the magic happens; your brain. You will look at some fascinating facts and discuss how you can help and take advantage of the power that your brain, or mind has.

Chapter 3

Your Brain

*"All sorts of bodily diseases
are produced by half-used minds."*

George Bernard Shaw

I was sent to the hospital in the fifth grade when my skin and eyeballs turned yellow and I started vomiting. Doctors suspected hepatitis but I was diagnosed with a liver disorder causing my bilirubin, the yellow-colored waste remnants of old red blood cells, to spike under certain circumstances. I was placed on a very strict diet. I could eat nothing that had any fat in any form. This meant giving up almost every food possible. My diet became very dry and boring.

I remember how sad I was that Christmas because there

was no traditional Christmas treat I could eat. If I broke my special diet, it meant instant vomiting that didn't stop--to the point of fainting. I didn't dare cheat. Soon, even the foods I always loved to eat looked unappetizing.

The good news for me was that sugar counteracted my vomiting. As long as I was able to keep sugar in my stomach for few minutes, it went into my bloodstream and I was fine. This was a challenge, but within minutes I got better and within an hour I looked as healthy as any child.

As a kid, I learned how fast my body reacted to food. My hands got slapped so fast, metaphorically speaking, and the consequences so uncomfortable, that my parents didn't have to worry that I would try a bite of food while visiting my friends. If I skipped two meals, I would get sick, too. It started slower and the throwing up was easier to stop with a few bites of pure glucose.

By the time I was in high school I learned that if I wanted to avoid some event, I could simply fast for few hours, get temporarily sick and quickly better. I didn't use this very often because it wasn't fun. However, I do remember skipping a school day and school trips on purpose. Maybe that was my first conscious step in leading my body into sickness and immediately out of it.

In some situations, you've learned to listen to your body. Like when you need to use the bathroom. You listen because the consequences of not listening are embarrassing and uncomfortable.

But when it comes to the environment, diet or exercise, those changes in your body are subtle and slow. You don't pay attention until the problem becomes so big that reversing it takes a lot of time and visits to the doctor's office.

The United States Department of Labor, Occupational Safety and Health Administration lists stress as a wide healthcare hazard. Stress is the cause of most of our problems. My friend, a psychiatrist, concludes that most all disease is caused by it. Medical research supports that over and over again. Even little babies are subjected to stress that is transferred from the mother to the baby inside or outside of the womb.

Sometimes stress can be helpful in keeping us healthy or alive. The episode with my liver happened two months after a terrible car accident I was involved in. My mother got half of her face shredded and I spent eight hours in a state of shock yelling at my bleeding mom not to die. According to doctors, I was predisposed to the liver disorder. However, it took that level of a stress to cause this to come alive from that moment on.

My mom claims that my reaction saved her life. She didn't want to die in arms of her ten-year-old daughter. From a medical point of view, she had no chance. Stress was what kept my mom alive and lucid for eight long hours before she got help. Her brain sent a message to the adrenal glands to kick in a massive dose of adrenaline and cortisol.

Stress, shock, and pure joy are reactions that happen in the body/mind's main office, the mighty brain.

When I worked as a personal trainer, I measured people's body mass index and calculated their calorie output versus calorie input. I don't think it's possible to have a completely accurate assessment. Up to 20 % of our energy is consumed by the brain. And that is hard to measure unless the person receives a brain scan.

It is hard to figure out how much thinking a brain does in a day. Nothing in your body needs as many calories as your brain for its size.

Neurologists are living in a golden age of discovery.

The study of the brain has never received such a scientific boom as it has in the past decade. The best thing is that you can profit from it.

The brain is a very hungry organ. Why does it need so much energy? Until recently, most scientists believed that the energy was used to fire electrical impulses between neurons. Turns out that this is not entirely true.

The National Academy of Sciences in the Unites States has a new study showing that two-thirds of our brain's energy is used to fire signals between neurons and glial cells, the two kinds of brain cells. One-third of the brain's energy is used for cell-health maintenance. One of the co-authors, Wei Chen, refers to it as "housekeeping."

Sodium, calcium and potassium atoms or ions are continuously traveling for the brain's needs. The brain is your mind's main office. And one-third of its budget is used to keep the brain tidy, healthy and ready to communicate in stand-by position. All you have to do is to know how to utilize it.

You listen to your body to some degree. You know when your stomach is telling you to eat or to sleep when you are tired. Sometimes you listen to these messages better than other times. People who neglect these messages can have a misunderstood relationship with their bodies. Addictive substances or behaviors that constantly tickle the pleasure/pain reward system hijack the brain.

Entrepreneurs who sleep 4-5 hours a day often suffer from insomnia. It is possible to live with 4-5 hours of sleep, be healthy and not suffer from insomnia. At least according to the mighty serial entrepreneur, author and self appointed guinea pig, Tim Ferriss.

I agree. You need to give your body some extra care in return. You have to treat your body with love and truth.

The best way to do that is in meditation. This is where science and spirituality are both connected. Although the belief in why it works may be different, there is no question that it works.

Being able to relax your mind and brain is the most important and hardest part about your mind/body connection. If you can spend moments in meditation or prayer, you have the tool to hear your body talk to you.

It's all about energy. The energy tool is mostly in your brain. Your conscious and subconscious mind can fight for the power. They need to be on the same page, want the same results, and put in the effort to work together. The subconscious always wins in the end.

The fact that energy affects and plays a role in the creation of mass is one of the biggest and most famous discoveries made by the genius, Albert Einstein, $E=mc^2$. E is the energy, M stands for mass and C is the speed of light in a vacuum.

Your brain has five states of consciousness, Alpha, Beta, Delta, Gamma and Theta. Each of these states impacts your body differently and is able to receive messages in a unique way.

Much of the time, babies and toddlers are in the Delta state. Their brain waves have a different length that can be seen in an MRI. They react differently to situations. I will talk about this more in the Chapter Ten. The messages their minds produce influence their bodies strongly for the rest of their lives. Ever hear that the first five years of a child's life are the most important?

Maybe your parents rewarded you with candy when they were happy with you. Now you reward yourself with food whenever you feel threatened by the world and are in the need of some love.

Sugar is a highly addictive drug that makes your synapses tap dance madly. You are almost guaranteed to be overweight forty years later if you become addicted as a young child. The pain/pleasure reward system inside your brain is like a trap. Messages from your body get traded for a bit of oxytocin or other pleasurable substances. Drugs are addressed in Chapter Five.

Things like sugar or aspartame can give your body misleading instructions about how to utilize the food and what is good for the body to ingest. It becomes the norm and you repeat the negative eating habits for years and sometimes your whole life.

It doesn't mean that you cannot enjoy a sweet dessert now and then. It means that you need to be very clear about what the pleasure substances can do to you and not allow them to take over your brain.

The energy that your brain produces is phenomenal. Electrical impulses fire messages created by your conscious and mostly by your subconscious mind.

The subconscious mind has the true power. That's why using willpower to achieve anything is almost a guaranteed failure. In the book "Beyond Willpower," the author, Alexander Loyd, PhD, ND, gives the conscious mind one chance in a million to win over the subconscious mind.

Why are there a handful of people achieving their unreal goals with willpower? I think it's because their conscious minds are working on something that is already set in their subconscious minds. That's why when people grow up and follow the professions that they wanted as kids, they are happy and often go further in achievement. If your body gets the right messages during your early childhood, you are one of the lucky ones.

However, there is a way to communicate with your body, to set new rules that are in harmony with you and your bodily needs at any point of your life. Meditation is the first and the most important key to unlocking the power. Chapters Ten and Eleven are focused on the practical cultivation of the mind.

In this chapter you learned about your fattest organ, the brain--the place where your body is granted audience with your mind. How it is important for your conscious and sub-conscious mind to be on the same page. It may take some fine-tuning which can be cultivated in meditation. It is vitally important to pay attention to your mind and what triggers your pain and pleasure programming.

In the following chapter you are going to have a look at your amazing zoo of little organisms. Let's find out what you have on your side to help, as well as what is in need of your guidance. It's time to farm!

Chapter 4

Farming Your Body

"Each of us is a unique thread, woven into the beautiful fabric, of our collective consciousness."

Jaeda DeWalt

Taking care of your body is like farming. You are trying to keep all the microbial communities that live in almost every part of your body happy so you can benefit from their hard work. They are quite primitive life forms that have been on this planet longer than any other.

These communities are really good at doing what they know how to do. Direction is needed with new, unknown tasks. For the most part, these organisms can learn anything that is in their capacity to learn. They are found in groups by the millions. I like to characterize their mentality as collective consciousness.

Collective consciousness is something that we can easily see in insects like ants or bees. The older the organisms are on the evolutionary scale, the more they are operating in collective consciousness and less in individual decision-making.

Animals fascinated me as a child. When I was in a middle school, my older sister brought me home three rare walking sticks that her friend's father brought home from his trip to the Middle East. I had no special food for them. Nobody knew what kind of walking sticks these were.

I contacted the best entomologist at the university with a description of my walking sticks. He sent me to a specialist. When I contacted him, he couldn't believe that this kind of walking stick was in the country. Meanwhile, I had to find a way to feed and take care of them.

As a kid you don't tend to complicate things. You come up with solutions quickly. I knew they needed leaves and whatever they would eat had to be available year-round. The only things available to me that could stay green even under the snow were strawberry leaves. So I started to feed these leaves to my walking sticks.

They were so happy that they laid eggs. When the eggs hatched, I was stuck with over 200 babies! My room needed two aquariums and 35-gallon jars. I was able to give a few walking sticks to my friends. For some reason, the walking sticks I gave away didn't breed like mine did.

My father was mad about the mini-zoo that took over my room. One day he tossed them all on our strawberry patch. I didn't know until it was too dark outside to retrieve them. My rescue mission started in the morning. I went on a careful hunt praying to find as many as possible. I knew they were tropical and didn't have long to survive. I found almost all of them, except four. To say the least, my father never did that again. I learned about better cleaning practices and quantity control.

How did I find hundreds of winged insects dumped in the wild hours later? I knew them all. And no matter what anyone says, I knew they had a relationship with me. I knew their behavior and I could easily spot them despite their brilliant camouflage. They were special with one pair of beautiful pink translucent wings. Unlike other walking sticks, they could glide. I let them out in my room often. They would fly around and look like six-inch fairies.

Taking care of your body well and creating a relationship is quite similar. When you understand the needs, potentials and limitations of the microorganisms, you can utilize it. No doctor can be inside your body. People can give you general advice. Nobody but you will ever feel what you can.

You have to be a good and kind master. Love and truth are essential skills. Let these awesome organisms become the best versions when they reproduce. To be a good master means to listen to the needs of the ones that depend on you. It is your mind that brings food to your mouth or decides that you are too tired today to do any exercise. It is a good thing to be educated about food, lifestyle and exercise. What kind of food is good for you and why? There are plenty of books and information about this everywhere. My goal isn't to bring awareness about some supplement or food, rather to bring awareness about what is good for you on an individual level. Few rules will remain the same for all of us.

Your body is awesome. It has kept you alive up to this point. And the level of help you get is phenomenal. Microbiome organisms may be little but without them, you would not even be here. They extract vitamins and other nutrients, tune up your immune system and even produce helpful anti-inflammatory compounds and chemicals that fight off invader bugs that make you sick.

The Human Microbiome Project was a project of mapping out the body and habitats. Two hundred scientists spent five years studying the complex ecosystem of a healthy human body. They found over 10,000 different species of microorganisms, many of them never described before. Your own body is a walking zoo and botanical garden that may be less explored than the moon.

What else did scientists find? I've already stated that there are ten times as many microorganism cells than human cells. There are 360 microorganism genes for every single human gene. The composition of microbes and the kinds of genes that they have are very much habitat-specific. Microbes on your skin and hands differ from other parts of your skin as well as microbes in your stomach.

Are you feeling like a farmer yet?

Taking care of tens of thousands of species can be overwhelming. It is just as overwhelming for microorganisms to deal with things you might throw at them. For thousands of years they have dealt with the same matter. Human lives were simpler in a sense of what was available. Now you have the world at your feet. You can taste all kinds of different cuisines without ever leaving your own town. You have complicated the demands on your farm. Preservatives, pesticides and food coloring have been added to your diet as well as genetically modified organisms. I will talk about them more in detail in a Chapter Six.

How are these primitive colonies living on and inside your body supposed to know how to cope? Can they learn and adapt? Yes and no. They can learn and adapt to something that already exists in their inherited 'handbook.' If something unknown calls for writing an entirely new chapter, the colonies are faced with something quite different.

People argue that artificial food coloring or chemical pesticides are something presented in a meal in extremely minute amounts. That may be true from our perspective. But from the perspective of microscopic bacteria, the amount that appears minute to us becomes very large to them.

I believe it is the same if your body doesn't know about some super food. It takes time to learn how to extract all of the beneficial properties. If you eat a new fruit or a supplement for the first time, your body absorbs only what is known. I absolutely don't want to discourage you from searching new, good food for your body. Keep in mind that the longer you eat the same thing, the better your body utilizes it.

Years ago I went on a hunt to find the best food for my dog. There were all kinds of data on the Internet about what was best for a dog. I researched an exhausting amount of data about canine digestion. And although I chose the raw meat diet for him, I knew that this was only part of the picture.

The longest living dog on this planet was a vegan his whole life. His owner was vegan so she fed him mostly rice and beans. He lived to be over twentyseven years old! Based on many claims about what was right to feed the dog, both rice and beans weren't supposed to be good at all.

Where's the catch? His diet was consistent. Made fresh with simple basic ingredients. And of course the base of his diet was the same as his owner's. Which, I concluded, played an important role for the dog as well.

Is the human body like that? I fully believe so. People residing in high places with the longest life expectancy eat a repetitive diet and are active their whole lives. They have good social encounters and strong bonds with their families.

The top five locations for the ultimate longest-living people on Earth are by the sea--Japan and the Mediterranean, or very high in the mountains all over the world.

The sea offers a very beneficial diet. It is hard to guess whether this will stay the same or whether the pollution of our oceans will change that. The quality of seafood has changed rapidly over the past couple of decades. Also much of the farmed seafood is known to do more harm than good for us. If you eat seafood, be sure to know its source.

Mountains offer a lower oxygen level. We need oxygen to live. Without it we would die within minutes. Why is low oxygen beneficial? From the long-term standpoint, the oxygen level in our blood is corroding us from the inside and hugely contributes to the aging of our organs. People in mountains generally have a more physically active lifestyle. Their organs stay more preserved. And the diet is very much the same year after year, even with the variation of seasonal change.

One of the longest living groups of people live in the mountains of France in a dairy farming community. They eat, almost exclusively, raw milk, meat and potatoes or wheat products. Interestingly, they consume hardly any fruits or vegetables. Yet they are very healthy and live long lives.

Most animals eat a very repetitive diet. Some live their whole lives on a single ingredient. The diet of the giant panda bear in the wild consists of 99% bamboo. Since they technically belong to the animal order of carnivores, a panda might eat a small rodent occasionally.

I believe the key to healthy living is a simple consistent diet that is free from artificial anything. Food should be prepared fresh without altered ingredients as much as possible.

Milk should be whole and also the products made from it. What you choose for your body as base ingredients in your diet is really up to you. Your bacteria will learn how to utilize it and will feed your body. The more often you present the same ingredients to your body, the more efficiently the microfauna can extract the nutrients for your human cells. Of course, if milk isn't treating you well, don't drink it.

Feel like a vegan? Be one. Feel like a bacon eater? Consume more bacon. Just make sure that it's free from nitrites and other unnatural ingredients.

What is good for your body is uniquely yours. However you should educate yourself about the food you eat and strive for high nutritional value. If you had to take out half of the food ingredients you eat now, what would you give up? What would you keep and why?

For the next week try this exercise. This is also great to do during your observation time and best when written down. Pick one meal a day to be the exactly the same for the next week. These are the conditions:

1. It must be lunch or dinner.
   Dinner is better because it's close to your rest time.

2. It cannot contain sugar or artificial sweetener as any ingredient, not even ketchup.

3. Complex starches such as pasta, potatoes or rice are fine, but they shouldn't be more than half of your meal. Less is better. Ingredients from sprouted whole grain should be used in place of flour.

4. Don't use products made with white flour.

5. Fruit (not juice) and honey are fine in any amount.

6. Don't drink alcohol with this meal. The minimum alcohol content in kombucha or fermented drinks is fine.

7. No ingredient can be genetically modified. You can read more about GMO's in Chapter Six.

8. Pick something that you really like and can prepare easily.

I would suggest you have something fermented in this meal. It is not necessary, but foods such as sauerkraut, whole milk yogurt or kombucha as a drink are treats for the microorganisms in your body. They aid digestion and help bring valuable enzymes into your body. You can choose any of many fermented foods or drinks and have just a small amount.

If you are eating like this already, for example taking the same lunch to work all the time, you know how much you are about to eat, right? If the meal is the same, it doesn't excite your brain like a new meal would. It shouldn't contain any kind of food drug that makes you eat more than you need. The microorganisms in your body can easily break this food down and utilize it better.

When you feel genuinely full, not stuffed, stop eating. And don't eat for at least four hours before and after this meal. Not even a snack, only water or unsweetened non-carbonated beverages.

People often have the tendency to eat more than they should. Pay attention during this week when you feel full. Did the same amount of food fill you for the whole seven days? Did the amount gradually decrease? Your body is sending you messages. Receive them. Act on them.

In this chapter you learned about your human body and the microorganisms that inhabit it, inside and out. You should understand the importance of keeping all of these microorganisms happy. Your brain can easily get tricked, so it is important to stay aware of how your body feels.

In the next chapter you will learn about drugs. The obvious drugs as well as those that are highly addictive that you may not consider as drugs.

Chapter 5

Drugs

"Drug (noun): a medicine or other substance which has a physiological effect when ingested or otherwise introduced into the body."

Oxford Dictionary

Using this definition, even food is a drug. Are we all addicts? Maybe. Let's look at drugs in this chapter.

The chances are that to some degree you are addicted to something. It may not be harmful and it can actually be beneficial to you.

For example I am a tea drinker. For years I have started my day with a beautiful cup of Earl Grey tea. Most likely I am a caffeine addict in a way that is presented in black tea. Somehow that doesn't apply to coffee for me. Quality black tea if properly brewed is very healthy and has many beneficial properties, so I don't have any desire to stop drinking it.

Not every drug is necessarily bad for you. I wouldn't suggest that you try to get rid of any drugs unless you are feeling a true urge to do so. It is important that you first gain the trust of your body. From now on please understand that when I speak of the body, I also mean all the microorganisms that reside in and on it. They are the ones who are in symbiotic relationship with you.

Let's separate drugs into two basic categories: one category adds calories or fluids to your body and the other doesn't.

As I mentioned earlier, a drug can be any food. Food has physiological effects when ingested. And to some people it can be addictive. Overeating is a problem for many people, often derived from childhood or even time in the womb.

If this is your case, know that it's honestly not your fault. Most importantly, it is not the fault of your body. Staring in the mirror thinking bad thoughts about your body won't help you connect to it. Your body deserves compassion and in most cases even an apology. It is doing it's best under the circumstances. It always is. But it can do only so much without proper guidance from a farmer with tender loving care.

Food addiction is one of the worst kinds of addiction. You have to eat to stay alive as opposed to drinking alcohol or smoking cigarettes. However even a food addiction is possible to conquer by identifying and eliminating the trigger foods.

Sugar is an extremely addictive drug that is presented in our daily life in more hidden ways than we care to acknowledge.

Society has the tendency to create new sugar addicts in children. Studies suggest that complex sugars presented in flour and potatoes can be even harder to quit than pure sugar itself.

It is no surprise that consumption of sugar can lead to obesity, type-2 diabetes, hypertension, cardiovascular disease and more. The brain reacts to sugar as it does to heroin or cocaine. A brain scan of a person on cocaine looks almost identical to the brain scan of a person on a sugar rush.

The speed of creating an addiction to sugar is staggering. Some studies claim sugar addiction to be five to eight times faster than to cocaine. We become addicts and then we create addicts of our children.

Every holiday is an opioid party.

Just one hundred years ago, an average American con-sumed about two pounds of sugar per year. Now that number is close to 160 pounds of sugar per year. That is almost half-a-pound per day! Americans are by far the number one nation in sugar consumption. We were taught that fat is bad. So it was replaced with sugar. Up to 80% of all prepared meals in the U.S. contain sugar. That makes it hard to avoid. Microorganisms working in your body extract sugars based on the source. To understand normal sugar use we need to understand that it is composed of two parts; glucose and fructose.

Glucose supplies pure energy that can be used by almost all of our organs and muscles. Glucose was what I needed when my liver gave out and it saved me. It is given in hospitals directly into your bloodstream when you are weak. Some-times we refer to it as blood sugar.

Fructose is found in fruits and vegetables as well as in normal sugar. Fruits and vegetables contain more water, fiber and vitamins. The sugar release is much slower and therefore the effect on the body is different.

Fructose is also part of regular sugar and things that hide under different names like corn syrup, evaporated cane juice etc., but in the end they are sugar.

Only the liver metabolizes fructose. This causes deadly fatty liver when consumed in excess, especially in a form that was stripped of fiber or water in its process. Sadly, that means that even juice would be just like drinking sugar water with added vitamins and possibly enzymes. Eat fruit as it is. Your liver can deal with juice, but it turns it into fat and stores it with toxins in your body. Fructose in excess is the bad guy. Refined sugar is sent to your bloodstream fast. It is made of about equal parts of glucose and fructose. It affects your brain pathways in a form of the famous 'sugar rush.' More complex sugars in the form of starch are released in a similar fashion, although a bit slower.

Your body welcomes honey differently. Despite the fact that honey contains 82% sugar and half of that is fructose, it contains a little bit of fiber so it is released into the body at a slower rate than sugar. It also contains vitamins and minerals and if raw, helpful enzymes rich in antioxidants that aid digestion. Interestingly enough, honey doesn't add to your waistline due to its lower glycemic index.

Every kind of honey is different. The different regions and times of the year may be helpful for some problems better than others. Just like your body is individual, so is honey. And honey may not be best for every person either.

Sugar, just like any drug, has a withdrawal effect. Some effects can be lowered or eliminated by gradually stopping the use of sugar instead of quitting cold turkey. Nonetheless, sugar is extremely bad for your body and should be used only in small amounts.

Aspartame, an artificial sweetener, has worse withdrawal effects. Artificial sweeteners have terrible effects on the body and mostly on the brain, all for an illusion that you won't add to your waistline. Over 900 studies show the dangers of aspartame. Contrary to popular belief, studies have found that artificial sweeteners actually add to your weight by stimulating your appetite, increasing carbohydrate cravings and fat storage.

Weight gain studies show a much greater risk for very harmful diseases when using artificial sweeteners. Migraine is the most common side effect and that's just the beginning. Harvard University conducted one of the largest studies that linked artificial sweeteners to cancer and active cancer-promoting cells.

The effect on your brain is devastating. Phenylalanine and aspartic acid are the main parts of aspartame and function as stimulants to brain cells that can get overstimulated to the point of death. Too much phenylalanine can cause serotonin depletion and make us sad or depressed.

If you are using artificial sweeteners, it will be important to let them go if you want to be able to listen to your body's needs. Your brain is the main office. If you can switch to honey, agave syrup or in the worse case, sugar, it is better than artificial sweeteners. I know sugar is another drug, but trust me on this. The side effects of sugar withdrawal are smaller and can be lessened gradually as you decrease your sugar consumption. Honey doesn't have that effect.

You can also switch to stevia or another natural sweetener, although moderation applies even here. I am not a fan of creating false information or tricking your body or brain. An illusion of sweetness isn't being truthful.

I said at the beginning of this chapter that I won't ask you to quit drugs just yet. Well, in the case of artificial sweeteners, I have to make an exception. The reason is that you need the part of the brain that helps you communicate signals to your body and your little helpers. It is almost impossible if you are using any artificial sweeteners.

If you are one of the people who drinks or eats sugarfree products, try to eliminate them. If you don't have a medical condition that forbids you from using honey, agave nectar, coconut nectar or even sugar, try to switch now. Make a journal where you can write the effects you experience. You may feel some withdrawal effects—headaches, migraines or mental problems such as mood swings.

Sometimes even weight loss is a side effect of coming off sugar-free products. However for some people, if they function as appetite-suppressants, there may be increased food cravings at a normal level. Cheer up. For the most part, within two weeks this should be over and your mind clearer.

Alcohol is another drug that in excess harms the liver and other organs. However there are many studies showing the benefits of two alcoholic beverages, wine and beer. Some studies show the benefits of moderate drinking of some spirits.

Still the recommended dose is one glass per day. Red wine is attributed to lower cardiovascular disease. The countries known for their higher consumption of wine do have fewer heart attacks compared to nondrinking countries. This is known as the French paradox due to their large consumption of butter and cheese that are known for increasing the chances of heart attacks. Wine companies heavily support this fact.

However, the benefits of alcoholic beverages occur only when taken in small quantities and interestingly enough, regularly. This again supports my theory of keeping the diet the same in order to get the true benefits from food. The Health Professionals Followup Study spent twelve years recording the drinking habits of thirty-eight thousand men. The results showed a 30-35% decrease in heart attacks in moderate drinkers.

Good beer is full of B vitamins that are received by your microorganisms with applause due to the fermentation process. So far I have not run into a fermented food that would not benefit the body.

Weight loss is close to impossible if you don't stop drinking any alcohol during this process. Alcohol is a poison for your body. And your body reacts to it. You have to teach your farm with a small quantity in order get the benefits. But don't count on weight loss being one of them. Your little microorganisms inside get drunk and don't really know what to do. You know what happens when you drink too much at one time? Your guts are not used to handling that.

Caucasians handle alcohol much better because their genes have been used to it for the longest time. Europeans used alcoholic beverages as a safer form to get fluids. Water was often contaminated and alcohol was safer to drink. Ancient wine was weak in alcohol content compared to modern wines, but it was also consumed all day long.

In Asia, the water was stripped of harmful bacteria by boiling and making tea. That's why Asian descendants are often less tolerant of alcohol and may get drunk after a single drink. With alcohol as with many other things, this is a very personal choice and in most cases I am sure you know how much and how often you can drink.

As I mentioned earlier I am a tea drinker. I believe that if you drink good quality tea that is properly brewed, it's healthy for you. Although caffeine is an addictive drug, it doesn't seem to stop me from being able to communicate effectively with my body. After years of drinking black tea, my body rejects teas of poor quality or if brewed for longer than five minutes. I also don't meditate within a couple of hours of drinking tea because it is a stimulant.

Coffee is another stimulant. Compared to tea, it's much higher in caffeine. Most importantly, caffeine is chemically different. Coffee, like tea, tends to create physical and habitual addiction. It's not too bad if your physical condition is good and you have a strong heart and drink in moderation. Coffee is a neurological stimulant. When you are going to communicate with your body don't do it after a double-shot latte.

Not every drug adds calories to your body. But a drug can affect the body in the way it deals with food or how muscles react to exercise. We talked about it with artificial sweeteners. Other things like pharmaceutical pills may have a similar effect.

The medicines that are bought over the counter or especially the prescriptions from your doctor are, in most cases, designed to alter the natural pathways in your body. Most often they disarm the body's selfhealing mechanism and rock the balance inside the body. That is sometimes very hard to get back.

In some cases pharmaceutical help is extremely important because your own healing system isn't engaged or may be broken and the journey of selfrepair may be taking too long. I do not want to discourage you from taking medication that may be vital to your health.

Frequently pharmaceutical medication has other unwanted reactions in the body and in many cases it doesn't allow the body to heal itself. While you are on a journey to communicate with your body and learn how to turn your body into a self-healing machine, be mindful of pharmaceutical medication and use good judgment and consult with your doctor.

In my case, I was able to get off all medications and mostly off antibiotics that were prescribed for me many times a year. For the purpose of self-healing, all medication that suppresses and doesn't heal the symptoms should be dropped. Taking painkillers or cough suppressants when your body is screaming at you to pay attention is counterproductive when you are trying to build trust between your mind and body.

This is a very sensitive area of decision-making. Not everyone in every circumstance may be able to do that. The timing should be right for your body and especially for your mind.

I don't know you. I don't know your condition or if your life depends on some prescription drug. Or if that drug makes your life depend on it. Your judgment must not be based on this book alone. However, this book should raise your awareness.

In the words of a former Pharma representative, Gwen Olsen, "Pharmaceutical industry isn't in the business of health and healing. It's in the business of disease management and symptoms maintenance." Gwen Olsen was a big Pharma representative until her own teenage niece quit taking psychiatric medication and ended her life by pouring oil on herself and setting herself on fire.

Do not ever quit medication that is supposed to alter your brain function in a single moment. One-in-ten Americans is on some kind of antidepressant or mindaltering drug. These are very dangerous. Psychological problems need to be treated. Pills aren't the answer in most cases. They turn people into addicts and quitting them may be life- threatening.

I find this most disturbing for children who are often put on ADD medication, or other mind-altering medications that are addictive. Proper diet, exposure to nature, and exercise can go a long way in helping these conditions in children. Pills can have dangerous consequences for a child, even to the point of suicide. Gradually lowering your child's intake of medication is the only safe way to insure health.

According to Richard Taite, the director of the rehabilitation facility, Cliffside Malibu, every nineteen minutes someone dies in the USA from an accidental overdose of prescription drugs. Legal drugs cause more deaths than all of the illegal drugs combined.

Although the United States contains only 5% percent of the world population, it consumes 75% of all legal medication produced in the world. Do you really think this is an appropriate amount?

I was put on opiates in the fourth grade. I have very little trust that doctors and pills can help me with disease. You may want to question them, and my statements as well. Think for yourself. No one else will do that for you.

Cannabis is another drug that has tendency to affect your digestive system.

I would like to note that I am writing this book in Oregon, a state where medical and recreational use of cannabis is allowed. Please follow the law of the state or a country you are in.

From a medical standpoint, Cannabis is amazing. It provides

incredible healing properties and our bodies are already equipped with the endocannabinoid system (ECS). Yes, that's right.

You have been born with cannabinoid receptors in your brain as well as throughout the central and peripheral nervous system. You create your own cannabinoids. Because ECS is involved in large variety of physiological processes, imbalance of cannabinoids in your body can cause all kinds of problems.

I see the extreme benefit cannabis can have for the right people. There are people who should not consume this plant at all. Without doubt, this plant has incredibly unique relationship with us.

If you try to lose weight, I wouldn't recommend cannabis. Studies show a high increase in foodseeking behavior known to users for a long time as "the munchies." It creates your sense of hunger. Endocannabinoids selectively enhance cravings for sweets.

If you are reading this book to help your autoimmune system, you can find a lot of information about the effects of cannabis. It is a new industry to science. Research studies are happening with staggering speed. Cannabis is believed to be the healing drug of the future. It has been the healing drug for a number of problems for millennia.

I should mention cigarettes. There is no question about their danger to your body. I personally know people who are amazing communicators with their bodies and yet they smoke cigarettes. They heal many disease symptoms using their communicating mechanisms. Sadly, the high physical addiction of nicotine doesn't let them stop. Still, the respiratory system and other parts of the smoker's body suffer.
The nicotine addiction is very high and so is the health toll.

One in five deaths are attributed to cigarette smoking. Almost half a million people die every year in USA. That is only the official statistic.

Hard drugs have horrible effects on our bodies. There is no point in going much deeper because this book cannot help anyone using hard drugs.

In order to be able to listen to your body at the conscious and subconscious level, you have to gain your own body's trust. That takes a lot of love and a little bit of time. It is worth it. Letting go of the drugs that harm your body, and often your mind, should be done gently, but surely.

Now let's look at the goodies you can provide for your body in the form of food. What is the best food? How does your body receive food? Do ingredients play an important role if they are in a minute quantity? All this, and more, is discussed in the next chapter.

Chapter 6

Non-GMO and Organic Foods

"Russia must protect its citizens from the use of food derived from genetically modified organisms."

Vladimir Putin, Russian president

GMO stands for genetically modified organism. GMO's were created in the lab by inserting genes from one organism into another. Sometimes genes are deleted or mutated in order to reach the desired results.

There are several methods used in order to get inside the cell and alter DNA. Most common are using a gene gun, attaching the gene to a virus that can penetrate into the cell or by physically inserting the extra DNA into a host with a tiny syringe.

The whole genetic modification in the lab is a pretty new

industry. The first successful modification happened in 1973 that altered the DNA of a mouse. The first genetically engineered plant took another ten years to develop.

As of the writing of this book, these are the following GMO crops available for human consumption in the US: alfalfa, canola (rapeseed), corn, cotton, Hawaiian papaya, potatoes (starch), soybeans, squash, sugar beets and the newly created Chinook salmon also nicknamed Frankenfish.

In 1982, the Food and Drug Administration in the United States approved the first human medication produced by a genetically modified organism. Bacteria was genetically engineered to synthesize human insulin and prescribed to patients as the drug Humulin.

During the early 1990's, the first genetically altered tomatoes hit the US market. By now America flooded its market with GMO crops for human consumption, food and even glowing pets. GMO crops have covered this planet's farmlands with staggering speed. Ten percent of the world's croplands were planted with GM crops in 2010. Over 70 million hectares of GM crops are grown in the USA now, making it the country with the largest GM production in the world.

Over 79% of the world's soy and 70% of the world's cotton are genetically modified.

According to Whole Foods Market over 70% of prepared food in the US contains genetically modified foods including bread, cereal and ketchup. The list goes on and on.

Meanwhile, the European Union is holding back on GMO crops. Larger crops are grown in Spain and Portugal and most production is used for feed or production of biodiesel.

Russian president Vladimir Putin speaks very openly about

the danger of GMO crops. He banned them from Russia entirely and is ready to make Russia the world exporter of 'clean' food.

He isn't the only politician interested in the dangers of genetically modified organisms.

The United Kingdom's Prince Charles helped farmers in India who received GMO farming capabilities. A heavy campaign produced by the world leader in genetic modification in the United States caused an extreme failure in growing these crops. Hundreds of thousands of Indian farmers committed extremely painful suicides by drinking the chemicals bought from this company.

I will never understand why this didn't become a world-known phenomenon. Despite the amount of news, despite the Indian people crying for help to the world, our western civilization didn't care in my mind.

So are GMO foods safe for us? Independent scientific research says no. A strong link has been found to suggest that GMO foods develop cancer, cancer growth, infertility, allergies, multiple sclerosis, gastrointestinal problems and much more. For many people, this is very scary. Of course, the research funded by companies producing GMO food finds no harm.

I am personally a bit skeptical in trusting a company that has claimed the safety of their other creations such as Agent Orange, DDT and bovine growth hormone.

Let's look at the consumption of foods containing genetic modification. It's only a small fraction of DNA that is making some difference in this modified organism. To most people, DNA sounds like something from a scientific lab or schoolbook. We usually imagine a model we saw somewhere.

It feels too microscopic to make it easy to understand.

It's actually not always that small. You can extract DNA from strawberries and some other fruits with your kids as a project at home. It's an easy experiment and visible to the naked eye. You can Google DNA extraction from strawberries for instruction.

Now take the idea of DNA size and compare it to the size of the good bacteria in your body. Imagine you are holding a string of beads where each bead is one single fragment of DNA. How are good bacteria going to deal with the modified food? Or delegate what to do with it? Now the DNA size doesn't seem small at all, right? No wonder genetically modified organisms have an extremely negative impact in our gastrointestinal tract. This is the place that has the densest farm of microorganisms.

Changing DNA isn't like taking a red bead out of the necklace and replacing it with a green one. It doesn't mean that the green bead is stable in its position. Even companies that create genetically modified organisms take years to be what they call 'successful' at this.

The companies test their success by inserting an antibiotic resistant gene into the desired organism. They flood it with antibiotics to see if the modification was successful. Can eating a GMO food that has been modified to be resistant to antibiotics make us resistant to antibiotics when we need them?

Imagine you are the bacteria in your own body dealing with nutrient extraction. For example, you are a worker sorting fruit. Most of your life for generations your army of microorganisms sort apples, bananas or whatever fruit is common to them. Exotic fruits and vegetables from other climates, say papaya or mango, are introduced. You, as a microorganism, look at it, smell it, agree it's fruit and it makes some sense. You assess what to do with it because it's still a fruit. If you are going to start getting more of this fruit, you'd better become faster and more efficient. This happens with a new food that still follows a normal pattern of nature.

One day your microorganisms are supposed to sort an alien fruit. They have no idea what to do with it. It looks a bit like a fruit crossed with an animal. It doesn't have all of the normal characteristics of fruit. It looks more like a fruit, but it moves like an animal. I am sure you get the picture.

When you are eating GMO foods, you are killing your farm. Many studies have shown the harsh effects they have on your microorganism fauna.

It takes evolution to be able to adapt to something this new. In the process, the weak links disappear. We are in that process right now if you look at the staggering speed we are losing animal and plant species on this planet. There is no reason to put your body through artificially induced evolution when you don't have to.

In the large international study that was tuned into effects of eating GMO and obesity, professor Åshild Krogdahl of the Norwegian School of Veterinary Science explains: "A frequent claim has been that new genes introduced in GM food are harmless since all genes are broken up in the intestines. But our findings show that genes can be transferred through the intestinal wall into the blood; they have been found in blood, muscle tissue and liver in sufficiently large segments to be identified. The biological impact of this gene transfer is unknown."

This study concluded that feeding rats GMO corn for just 30 days made them gain weight compared to rats not fed GMO corn. In a different study, rodents fed on a GMO diet enlarged their stomachs and thus their sense of being full came later and they consumed more. With humans it is very likely to be the same.

I live in a small mountain town. Most of the people eat genetically modified organisms. Living here for fifteen years I have seen the change. Years ago, people here weren't that large and rarely obese. This has changed rapidly. The lifestyles of the locals are active. Weather keeps us on our toes half the year. Now there are several obese children in every class in school, from an early age. And it's not just because of their sugar intake.

My body rejects any GMO. I started avoiding them as soon as I learned about their existence many years ago. At the beginning, I was obsessed with research from scientists who lost their jobs due to their findings.

Years went by and I craved some authentic Asian food, which contains soy. I was starving so I gave it a shot. Only to almost bring it back to my plate from my stomach. My body rejected this food faster than I anticipated.

I actually tried it again some time later. Can I get away with eating something soaked in GMO soy sauce and fried in GMO soybean oil? Nope. My body goes on strike fast. Do I mind? Nope. I can cook what I want out of non-GMO ingredients. In today's market, shopping is a breeze compared to what was available a decade ago.

I know that when I eat in a restaurant, I may eat some food with GMO's. I still try to avoid it by Googling places to eat in a new town or sending the waitress into the kitchen with a list of questions. For the most part, I don't have any immediate reaction to GMO's presented in small amounts. What it does to my body over the long term, I don't know.

One fact remains regardless of anyone's point of view:

Eating non-GMO food is the only way to be sure that your body knows how to break down the food properly and how to utilize it.

So what is the best food for us?

In ancient times before we started to farm food, we hunted and picked wild plants. Wild harvesting gave us food that was obviously organic, had the best amount of nutrients and provided us with the exercise our body needed. This kept our senses sharp. There was a balance.

When humans started farming, they were still eating close to the same way. The food was still organic and there was a bit more security in that the food was available and not being consumed by wildlife. We didn't have to hike far to get it.

Organic farming was practiced until the middle of the last century, simply because pesticides and genetically modified organisms weren't invented yet. Our bodies were not meant to know what to do with anything artificial. Our microorganisms evolved millions of years ago and their evolution stopped. It wasn't needed until now.

Organic food is easy for your body to understand. It is the closest food to what you are meant to eat. I would highly recommend spending some family time in the summer and picking mushrooms or wild berries. I love the fact that we live in the twenty-first century and can freeze all the goodness we harvest from the wild.

I should be fair to some pesticides. There are some plant-based organic pesticides that do not appear to harm humans. You have to know where your food comes from or buy organic to be sure.

You have some information about how genetic modification is affecting your body, the people and this planet. Investigate further if you have more questions.

In the next chapter I'll show you how to switch the food you like into the organic version on a budget while gaining the trust and happiness of your body.

You won't have to change most of your favorite meals.

Chapter 7

Switching to Organic Food on A Budget

"Your diet is a bank account. Good food choices are good investments."

Bethenny Frankel

In a previous chapter we talked about toxins in the body. Because the body doesn't really know how to deal with them, it stores them.

In a beehive when something foreign gets in, bees remove it. If it is small enough for the bees to carry. If a mouse gets inside the beehive, the bees kill it.

They are stuck with something too big to remove. In order to maintain a healthy hive, the bees cover the whole body of the mouse with propolis which mummifies the mouse. There is no rotting mouse in the hive and no danger of consequences connected with the dead rodent's body in the hot hive.

The human body acts in a similar way with unknown, large toxins. A healthy body gets rid of the small toxins but some are just impossible to handle for the body. So the body covers these toxins with fat and stores them inside. The fat functions like the propolis in the beehive.

When you go on a diet and or start an exercise program, you are trying to get rid of the excess fat in your body. You are basically going to war with your body. You insist that the fat that is actually protecting you from the possible effects of the toxins is removed.

You can win this war and get rid of the unwanted fat. Short term. As soon as you let yourself go off the diet or your body adjusts to the amount of exercise, your body covers the toxins that are still inside you with fat again. This is known as the yo-yo effect. You gain what you had before and then add more fat on top. The body wins the war.

When you start to lose weight, toxins that are stored up in fat flood your blood. You may have experienced fatigue or feeling bad during weight loss in the past. Toxins are a huge part of that. The National Health and Nutrition Examination Survey followed 1,099 adults that were placed in five categories: stable weight, moderate increase and decrease and large increase and decrease. The survey monitored the six largest pollutants in the blood. The group of people who experienced the largest weight loss had about 50% more pollutants in their blood than the group of people experiencing the largest weight gain.

It is important not to add any more toxins to your body. To do that, you need to get rid of the bad ingredients in your food. You can still eat comfort food. Just cook it yourself and use good non-GMO food. Organic is the best.

I understand that switching to organic food is not cheap. However, it is doable even on a very small budget. I can also tell you that the cost pays you back by being healthier and more productive. You won't spend the money or time at the doctor's office.

The truth is that switching to healthier food doesn't even have to cost you more than it costs you for the food you eat now. It takes planning. This is an important step in the process for your health. You are trying to gain the trust of your body.

If you're like me, you have had a few battles with your body. By my late teenage years, I was able to exercise about half the time in a way I couldn't before. I trained twice a day and counted every calorie I ate. If I exercised only once a day or ate anything out of the ordinary, I gained weight.

This was about twenty years ago. Now I exercise two to four times a week in addition to my five-minute morning stretching. I eat what I feel like. Despite what everyone told me about the body change that was supposed to happen after giving birth to my daughter, I still fit in the same pants I wore the first day of high school twenty-five years ago.

I am no longer at war with my body. Instead I listen to what my body wants and I can make good decisions about how to act on that. If I end up going to a really good buffet, I ask my body not to store the excess calories as body fat. I go ahead and pig out without consequences. Of course I do follow this with healthy cleansing meals as soon as can.

You will be able to do the same when you become a good friend and a kind leader to your body.

As you know, your body needs to be dealing with known substances because it is easier for your farm. The better it understands what you feed it, the better job it does in utilizing the nutritional potential of your food.

You need to plan your organic and non-GMO meals in order to eat well without blasting your budget. Studies suggest that up to 40% of food in the USA ends up uneaten and tossed away. That is a lot of extra money for food that literally ends up in the garbage.

The easiest way to ensure that this won't happen is to create your weekly meal plan. This will also serve as a major help for your body. If you are eating the same meal for lunch or dinner as I discussed in Chapter Four, that's fine. It will only help.

Choose your preferred meal for your dinners throughout the week. This works best if this weekly plan repeats itself. However, you can always switch to a different meal. For example, every Monday you can have chicken stew, every Tuesday soup and salad, every Wednesday a bowl of chili and so on.

If you know what you are eating ahead of time, you can shop exactly for that food and eliminate almost all waste. Because you won't be throwing food away, you won't need to buy as much. This in itself will allow you to change all GMO foods in your diet to nonGMO foods and still be financially better off.

Unless you have a physically demanding job, you can eat less meat if it is too costly. Buy meat that is raised on a non-GMO diet. It is suggested that about size of a deck of cards is the size of meat a human needs per day. Personally, I think it's less for females and more for males especially during a productive age. Children until they reach puberty need far less meat than adults and so do elderly people.

It may take you a few weeks to nail down your shopping adventures, but it's worth it. Once you learn what you can eat, you won't need to read labels and your shopping trip will take a fraction of your time because you know exactly what you're getting.

Most people eat the same food for breakfast, if they eat breakfast at all. So planning this meal is easy. You need to make sure that your breakfast doesn't contain corn flakes that aren't organic or verified non-GMO. Can you keep your breakfast low on sugar? I would strongly suggest that your first meal of the day has a sufficient amount of raw food in order to deliver enzymes to your farm first. Even better is to start your day with raw fermented food. Show some love to your farm!

You do not have to change your eating habits. We are all individuals and what suits one person may not suit another. Maybe you will find yourself changing your eating habits on your own when your body needs it. I would not push a vegetarian to eat meat or vice versa.

In my family we all have different appetites. I try to compromise to a certain level and some meals I split into two pots to finish up differently. It is a better way to serve our individual needs without taking too much of my time.

Tastes changes with age and also with the season. I am sure that you tend to eat different foods in the heat of the summer than you eat in the winter. Your body is whispering to you. Different seasons, like different ages bring different needs for your farm. It is good to listen to that.

I like to make an extra portion of meals that freeze well and taste excellent when defrosted. This makes it easy to make food on a day when cooking is hard. I bake a few meatloaves at one time and freeze extras. When the time comes, I just put one back in the oven for a delicious and mess-free meal. Strong broths with some meat are another way to get a quick base for soup. I add some fresh vegetables and noodles, and a very fresh-tasting meal can be on the table with little effort required from me. Almost any sauce or anything liquid freezes well without diminishing the taste when defrosted. Play with it and I am sure you can create your own list of freezable meals.

Cooking in bulk and freezing individual portions also allows you to freeze the meal in something other than plastic. Plastic is very toxic and molecules of plastic transfer into our meals. It is almost impossible, even with caution, to keep small particles of plastic from running in your bloodstream at this very moment. Heat causes these molecules to transfer into meals much faster. Never heat a frozen meal in a plastic container in the microwave.

I freeze meals in Pyrex containers or in the mason jars. Heat resistant glass is an excellent way to store food and can be used in the oven as well. Remember that liquid expands when frozen by 10%. Leave extra room for that. Glass isn't forgiving like plastic that would stretch for this.

Is your lifestyle too busy to cook a big meal every day? Choose something that you like that's easy to prepare. Then you can take one day a week to cook in bulk something that you can freeze and reheat.

Consciously adding raw food into your diet also decreases your need to cook.

Bulk cooking saves you time with less waste. Buying in bulk saves money as well. Many big stores offer organic food in bulk and shopping online may be a great option when free shipping is offered. Sometimes it can be hard to justify buying a whole 30 lb. bag of rice when you need to shop for other food as well. Try to dedicate a portion of your spending to something you can buy in bulk every month.

There are many dry foods such as legumes or grains that can be stored for a long time when put into an airtight container and stored away from light. You can put the food you like to have on hand in smaller glass jars and store the big bags in a dry cool place--pantry, basement or garage.

There is one big benefit of storing good organic food. If you run into a situation when your finances are limited or needed elsewhere, your meals don't have to be compromised.

In my family we buy a quarter of a cow per year from a local farmer. This has a great benefit in so many ways. I know that the beef has been raised on pasture grass its whole life and is truly happy. I always have good meat on hand regardless of our financial situation at the moment. The whole year we are consuming burgers made from one single cow, unlike a hundred cows that make one hamburger from a commercial food chain. Seriously, check it out on Google.

Do you know your eating habits? Great! Do you munch throughout the day? Are you doing it because you are hungry or is it a habit you created?

I am not a big fan of munching food during the day. If I am not hungry, I don't munch. I find that munching is more my mind's need than my body's. Commercials affect this to an unbelievable level. Once you create a habit to munch popcorn when you watch a movie, you are going to have a hard time breaking it. Watch your habits!

You should be consciously aware of why you are munching. If it is for hunger, have a small meal. If it is just a habitual thing, replace it with fruits, vegetables, or unsweetened nuts. Small baby carrots can make a great snack to have when your hand automatically reaches for something while reading or watching TV.

Habitual snacking is hard to break. However, it is relatively easy to replace with better foods to snack on.

Because of what sugar does to the brain, I wouldn't recommend munching on anything sweetened by sugar and that includes corn syrup, agave nectar, or any sweetener.

Are you that person who eats sweets daily? Or does the super-shake for breakfast, salad for lunch, fifteen donuts and a pint of ice cream for dinner sound familiar? If you end up eating sweet things at night and you feel like you can't help yourself, it's because sugar is addictive and you need your daily dose. Being purely aware of that fact will make it easier down the road when you ask your body to get rid of that addiction. You will learn that in the next part of the book.

Right now don't worry about the sugar. As long as it is not genetically modified corn syrup, of course. Eat sweets for breakfast or the first half of your day. If your body is physically addicted to sugar, eat all the things that you would have at night in the morning. This way your body has a chance to use up the energy without storing it. And in the evening when this energy would have been stored as your body fat, you won't crave the sugary food.

Artificial sweeteners inhibit your brain's neurons and their ability to send signals to your body. I urge to even stop chewing sugar-free gums. The natural nocalorie sweeteners should be taken with precaution. You are always better off giving your body the energy that you are promising. It is very important to be true to your body. You can always use honey or coconut sugar that breaks down slowly and is processed differently.

It is important to be interested in the food you choose to eat. Research what your food has to offer. You should downsize the amount of food you are going to use to create your favorite meals. Replace ingredients with their healthier counterparts. For example replace bleached flour with sprouted unbleached flour; prepared spice mixes with individual spices. It isn't too hard once you get started. When you are eating just a few meals made of the same ingredients you won't need to spend too much time researching what you are eating.

Now that you know about switching to non-GMO and organic foods on the budget, you need to get rid of the toxins that are most likely stored inside your body. In the next chapter, I am going to share with you my favorite way to detoxify and adjust weight at the same time.

Chapter 8

Detoxifying Your Body

"Because we cannot scrub our inner body we need to learn a few skills to help cleanse our tissues, organs, and mind."

Sebastian Pole

In this chapter we are going to talk about detoxifying your body. Whatever the issue is that you would like to resolve with your body, it's best to do when your body is free of toxins. Two main things have to happen. First, you cannot be adding more toxins, and second, you have to clean up whatever is inside you.

I am going to offer you the system that works for me, and some information about foods that help. I have been using this system for a couple of decades successfully. I do not disregard the many good detoxifying systems out there, or the great supplements that help with that. Research and try anything else. The goal is to detox. The path you take should fit your needs.

Feel free to modify my system or return to it if modification doesn't work. You are an individual and our bodies are different. You need a general cleanup so you can start befriending a happy body. Just keep in mind that it is necessary to keep your meals made of real ingredients, from scratch if possible.

I have mentioned earlier that when a body needs to deal with large toxins, it covers it up with fat and stores it. When you force your body to get rid of the fat through diet or exercise, it ends up with toxins that need to be covered up again. In order to prevent the yo-yo effect from happening, you need to lose the toxins.

I found with my body that the season of the year plays an important role with my successful detox. Summer sounds appealing for a great detox, but it doesn't work for me. It offers way too many goodies that I want. I also move more, eat out more, and attend more events where food is served. Trying to stay focused on my meals is very hard.

This choice will be individual to you. If you struggle with the detox in the summer, do what you feel you can handle now and try again in a couple of months when the weather is different or you feel inside that you are ready.

I concentrate on detoxifying my body about once a year. Usually I have the best success in the winter. A few times I did it over Christmas and didn't even mind I was missing out on traditional holiday food. When it feels right to me, I try not to break the cycle until my body decides that it is cleansed. However, when it doesn't feel right, I don't push the detoxification past three days.

Early spring is also a great time for the detox for all who live in a seasonal environment that brings the first fresh food. It can get your body ready for all the beautiful local fruits and vegetables.

You don't have to go on any diet in order to be able to communicate with your body. However, going through a cleansing process speeds up communication and gives you energy to do it. You cannot be fully healthy if you are like a cupboard filled with toxic cans.

So if you have a big problem when you go through a food detox, you can adjust it, or leave it for later. If you do it now it will bring you results much, much faster. Think of this process as consciously making a statement to your body; I am aware and ready to listen.

During this time you should feel just a tad hungry, never starving, never really hungry. But also do not overeat. Concentrate on every meal you eat. When you are full, do not eat more. When you start to feel more than just a tad hungry and ready to eat, well go for it. Munch on raw vegetables to pass a little bit of time until your meal.

Give this regimen a shot for at least three to five days. It's normal that first couple of days your body protests. If it feels extremely hard to follow and you feel like you are fighting your body, don't do it now. If your body is accepting this, continue for two weeks or more if comfortable. It gets easier with time while the toxins are being reduced. Practice the following steps and do the body-cleanse before you practice the communication with your body that you will learn in Chapter Ten.

Now let's get to the cleanse itself. Here are the main rules to follow during the cleanse:

1. No starch without fiber.

2. No alcohol.

3. No products from white flour.

4. No sugar, corn syrup and other sugary kind of syrups. The only sweetener allowed is honey and even that should be under control during the 'omnivore' day.

5. Nothing artificial.

You can eat everything else. However, eat food only in two specific groups.

Group number one consists of meat, eggs, dairy products, fat derived from dairy or animals, vegetables, and small amounts of nuts, fruit, honey, and oils. Don't eat starchy foods like corn, potatoes, bread, rice and other grains and also legumes, including soy products.

Group number two consists of starchy foods like corn, potatoes, bread (must not be sweetened or from white flour), rice, other grains, tofu, and other non-GMO soy products, legumes, nondairy milk, vegetables, fruits, nuts, honey, oils. Foods in this combination are vegan. No meat, eggs, or dairy products in any form. Make sure to eat more vegetables than starchy food during the day.

You can combine any food within one group during one day. The next day you can choose if you want to eat food in that group again, or if you want to eat from the second group. You just have to stick with that food group during the whole day. This way your body doesn't become deficient in one kind of food.

You need to have more than 50% of raw food in your first meal of the day: fruit, vegetables, even sashimi. Ideally, keeping your diet at least 50% raw all day is an excellent way to speed up the detoxifying process.

If you are a person who tends to like meat, use group one for more days. A few days in a row are better than switching every day. If you tend to be more of a vegetarian, eat more days from group number two. I usually eat from group number one for three days or so and then one day from group number two to fill my needs for legumes and complex sugars.

Sometimes it's hard to decide in the morning which group sounds better. You can always have fruit or vegetables that are allowed in both days and choose later in the day. I often imagine, for example, oatmeal with fresh fruit and honey and then I imagine a small cob salad and choose what sounds better at the moment.

It's a really good idea to add food like seaweed or chia seeds that help to pull an amazing amount of toxins from your body. Sauerkraut and cabbage are great, too. Cacao without the refined sugar is excellent as well. Keep in mind that super-foods are amazing for those who eat them often enough that the body knows how to benefit from them. Fermented food in general is a great help to your GI track and I would recommend at least one fermented product per day.

It is very likely that during this time your body weight will shift towards the direction your body is supposed to be, especially if you stay on this cleansing diet for more than a week. Your body will start to rapidly adjust to its ideal shape. It is good to stay on this cleansing way of eating for about two weeks. By not having your body process certain food combinations, it will get a bit of free time to deal with the stored up fat and toxins. Some people may experience headaches and feelings of being tired. This has to do with the amount of toxins that are in your bloodstream. This should end pretty soon, within a few days usually, depending on your level of toxicity.

If your body is happy to keep eating this way after two weeks, don't stop until you want to. However, if it comes to the day that you feel that you no longer can do this and you feel that your body is fighting you, don't beat yourself up. Some discomfort is normal. Your blood stream is moving toxins through your body. Pushing yourself isn't worth it. When your mind and body are ready for the detox, you won't experience many problems.

This is a great time for self-observation. Feel free to check your weight in the morning. Don't judge yourself if you don't see any change or if there's a day when your weight spikes. The goal is to detoxify. When I cheat and eat forbidden food, such as something from flour or have an alcoholic beverage, I see a huge weight increase over one day. Don't worry and don't blame yourself. Add on a few days to your diet.

This way of eating may increase your bowel movement. It will eventually adjust. I need to point out here that your body uses your gastrointestinal track to get rid of most toxins. A lot of people think that they are going to sweat it away. Not likely. Going to a sauna will help to lose some toxins and I am fully for it, only don't expect all of your toxins to be lost through your skin. Make sure you drink plenty of water or healthy drinks such as coconut water. When you let your toxins loose, you want to flush them out with fluids.

You are waking up your herd of microorganisms and calling them out. Keep your food simple.

Be really careful about pre-made food and snacks. Read the list of ingredients. Most of the meals on the market contain a combination of both food groups. Quick snacks can be taunting. On the day you're supposed to eat meat, you might grab a handful of tortilla chips instead. This is often done with your subconscious mind.

Move all the snacks behind 'two steps'--meaning out of your direct reach. Make yourself aware of what you are doing by having to open a cupboard and then reaching for the snack. This should make you aware of your subconscious behavior. Notify your family members about this and don't let them have snacks out either. This doesn't apply to raw fruit and vegetables. Have a bowl of fruit right on your table.

Within a few days you should feel a difference in your energy level. You should also be more aware of what is going on inside you. Don't forget to keep a little notebook about what is happening and how you feel.

Maybe you are already starting to feel more connected to your body. If you are craving foods other than sugar, you are on your way.

Now that you know the importance of getting rid of toxins and how to do it, it is time that you learn an easy way to eliminate further intake of them. How to create an environment for mind-body communication will be the subject of the next chapter.

Chapter 9:

Simplify

"Simplicity is the ultimate sophistication."

Leonardo da Vinci

Most of my life I have been hearing that we should eat a great variety of food--all colors of the rainbow in the fruit and vegetable world. If I skip one color, I miss out on certain vitamins and nutrients. If that is true, I don't know how humankind has made it this far. Most of the animals in the animal kingdom are doomed if we subscribe to this assessment.

Take the koala for example. This marsupial exclusively eats a single kind of food -- Eucalyptus leaves. The leaves are extremely low in nutritional value and super high in fiber. The Koala is so picky that it eats only certain species of Eucalyptus leaves. How does the Koala get enough calcium to build bones or enough vitamins with such a poor diet? The microorganisms are so used to the same food that they know exactly what to do. The Koala's body is a perfectly organized machine.

Less known and a distant relative of primates, the Pen-tailed tree shrew is a small alcoholic. This tiny animal lives on naturally fermented nectar from the Bertram palm in Thailand. The little creature fits in the palm of your hand. Every night the tree shrew drinks the equivalent of ten to twelve cans of beer without any sign of intoxication. Living on this simple diet, a tree shrew is a perfectly happy, healthy species.

Can a low variety of food types be applied to the human body? This has been the case for thousands of years. Until humans started commuting and carrying food from one distant location to another, they ate simply.

My friend cooks chicken and rice for her husband every Sunday for the entire week ahead. That's what he has eaten for years, along with special shakes regardless of holidays or special occasions. It is a more radical approach, but I cannot deny that the results show. He is a fitness professor and teaches others how to become trainers.

Your body will function better and be more predictable when your diet is consistent. It is also the state in which your body and your mind have a clear road of communication.

You can find books on the market that promise you a healthier body if you eat the ten or fifteen ingredients that are identified in the book. Would this kind of diet work? Yes. In my opinion, a limited amount of ingredients is something so personal that in order to be able to enjoy the long-term effects, you have to choose the foods yourself.

Until about hundred years ago our diets changed with the

seasons. Inside these seasons, the food remained the same year after year. People worked hard on their small farms to feed their families and stored food in a way that was very beneficial.

Cabbage lasts a long time when made into sauerkraut. The fermentation process enhanced the cabbage. It is much higher in vitamin C and other beneficial nutrients that are not found before the process. Small bacteria make this possible, the same kind you need in your digestive system. That's why antibiotics can be so harmful to use as they kill the bad and good bacteria in your body. Their use needs careful evaluation.

The microbes inside your body can do amazing work with food if they know what they are processing. You are going to be better off eating blueberries from your garden than you would ever be eating goji berries that might be foreign to your body unless you live in China. If you want to eat them, take the time to learn how to process them by eating them every day. Goji berries travel thousands of miles to make it to your belly and a lot of advertised nutrients are going to be lost during transit.

When solid food is introduced into the diet of a baby, the mother is very careful. She tries one single source food like carrots and waits to see how the baby reacts to it. We are so careful with our babies when they are little, yet soon after they eat solid food, we start mixing everything up and giving them a rich diet of plentiful ingredients and sweets.

When my daughter was a toddler and I would travel home to visit my family and childhood friends, I was frustrated with the amount of sweets she was given by them. The hardest thing was that all of these people did it as an act of care and love. And I was the one who had to explain to them that I didn't give my daughter sugar at that point in her life.

Since childhood we are often rewarded with food. Did you ever hear "you can have a candy when you are done with your dinner"? Don't reward yourself or anyone with food. Don't give sweets as presents. Every body is precious and should be respected. Being true and loving to yourself and others will change your life forever.

Educate yourself about food. Start with food that you like the most. Learn its qualities and create your own diet from basic ingredients that you cook yourself. It is always better to cook your own meals because that way you can avoid preservatives or even food that is not fresh enough.

It is important that you have an idea about the natural remedies that are good for your normal problems. Your body will naturally crave the cure. I literally go in front of my collection of herbal teas and pick the one that my body craves. I drink it with honey.

There is a lot of great information on the Internet to help with this. You can bring the cost of food down to a manageable budget and still eat non-GMO foods. I have friends living on disability, or are in a lowincome bracket who switched to a 100%, non-GMO and mostly organic diet.

I know you can do it. We are being told from all sides what the best food to eat is. I am asking you to find out what the best food for you is. Make it simple. If you can make a dinner with no more than five ingredients you are doing great. When your grocery list is memorized simply because you know what you and your family need, you know you are on your way.

Try to create healthy and tasty choices. Don't complicate the food for your body. However do not compromise the taste and what you love to eat. As time goes on you will start making healthier choices naturally.

When you take the energy to study the few things you eat, you start to feel a different kind of craving. It's not a mind's craving. It's a different kind of craving for food that your body needs or is deficient in.

Keeping diet simple is my mantra. It will keep you healthy and within a budget. The high quality of food should not be compromised. Neither should you neglect providing enough fiber, protein, healthy fat, vitamins, and micronutrients.

I am very excited to share with you the next chapter. I thank you on behalf of your body. You are taking time to get rid of the toxins in your body, to eat simply and to buy organic food whenever possible.

You are ready to learn the amazing way to talk to your body and learning the language your body is whispering to you.

Chapter 10

Meditation

"Meditation is the antidote to all the poisons of your life. It is the nourishment of your authentic nature."

Bhagwan Shree Rajneesh

Meditation is a conscious practice to access your subconscious mind. It is a practice to direct your quiet thoughts or let them all go. Meditation is as old as humankind and maybe we are not the only species who practice it. Meditation in various forms is found in every religion or philosophical belief.

Your brain cells are creating electrical pulses that are fired between neurons and glial cells. An EEG, electroencephalogram, monitoring method can measure these pulses. At any moment, this method can show you all of the waves being fired in your brain.

Like a symphony your brain is playing beautiful music. Although a healthy brain in any moment plays in all notes. One frequency is dominant over all others. There are five types of brain waves that shape the state of mind.

Delta waves (0.5-3 Hz) are the slowest and loudest waves. Infants and little children are most likely to be in this state. As you age, you raise your frequency. Even in the deepest sleep, normal adults show very few delta waves. However, this is the state in which the body self-heals. In this frequency, all of your cells are rejuvenated. This state can be accessed in deepest meditation and should be your ultimate goal. I think that is why it is hard to judge the ages of Tibetan monks. They spend hours practicing meditation daily.

Theta waves (3-8 Hz) are dominant in sleep and deep meditation. You can find yourself in this state when you are drifting off to sleep. These are also great restorative waves that bring peace into your life. If a human brain shows too many theta waves at the wrong time of the day, it can cause depression or ADHD. When these waves aren't present enough, your brain causes you stress, anxiety and poor emotional awareness.

Alpha waves (8-12 Hz) are in the middle of your states of mind. They create bridges between your subconscious and conscious mind. They can be accessed during certain kinds of meditation. Alpha waves are dominant during thinking and give you the power of being present to experience the "now" and the feeling of relaxation.

Beta waves (12-38 Hz) are most common during your productive times. Your brain experiences beta waves when you need to focus on completing a task at work or school. These are generally the most desired waves in a productive day. Coffee and other similar stimulants help raise you to this state when you are mentally tired.

Gamma waves (38-42 HZ) are the fastest of all and are related to simultaneous information processing from different brain areas. People with learning disabilities show very little of these waves. These waves are pretty rare. However, they are very active during the feeling of universal love, altruism, and higher spiritual virtues. These waves cannot be fired by neurons. To the scientific world, it is not really clear how these waves are produced. In my opinion they are produced by glial cells that make up almost 90% of all cells in the brain. Early in the last century scientists dismissed the importance of glial cells saying they were only fillers next to neurons. That's where the myth that we use only 10% of our brain comes from. Only in recent years have glial cells been getting scientific attention and realization that they are far more important than we thought.

Think about life as an energy field where you are standing and exchanging information with everything and everyone.

I love to watch the TV shows with Cezar Milan, the Dog Whisperer. He teaches people exactly this and applies it to dogs. Not to meditate, but to lower the intense energy of the dog's owner, for it is at this stage that the dog listens. If you see any of his shows, you know that he often goes to the problematic dog and the dog does things for him within minutes that his owner claims are impossible.

Here is how meditation helped me in one instance.

I am a pet junkie. My whole family is. We have all kinds of creatures. Energy is the way to have a good pet without spending much time trying to teach them whatever rules you wish them to obey.

I remember one night when my husband returned from an event

in the middle of the night. My large seventy-five pound bulldog took the role of bodyguard whenever I was home alone. There were about six cars in our driveway that night with people moving and saying their goodbyes at 3 am. This was the absolute situation when my dog, Moxie, would go nuts.

Our daughter was asleep and I didn't want to face the consequences if she woke up. There was no way I could keep Moxie from barking by just giving him a command. I sat down and meditated. I recall the exact energy vortex in which I resided; Moxie was completely calm. I felt like I was in the middle of a positive tornado. He knew I was fine with the people outside. As soon as my energy shifted one tiny bit, he wanted to start barking. I was able to hold and feel this frequency for a good twenty minutes until my husband walked in the door and the other cars left. It was a huge 'aha' moment for me.

Meditation lowers the brain frequency from beta state into theta or another state of mind.

From the moment you wake up until you go to sleep, you raise your brainwaves to a higher frequency in order to keep up with your life. This also increases other physiological activities going on in your body such as breathing, heartbeat or muscle function.

Science isn't sure exactly why meditation works and how it heals the body and mind.

Sleep is a state where your brain and body are in similar frequency. Meditation is a state where you are fully alert about your surroundings and your body. It is the state in which you can receive information about yourself and ask your body to act as you wish. It is also a very fragile state and so important that you stay loving and kind to yourself during meditation. During meditation you open up the pathway between your conscious, subconscious mind, and body. This is the frequency in which most of nature communicates. Something that is practiced regularly actually creates more brain matter.

Have you ever heard the saying that people will often forget what you said, but they won't forget how you made them feel? This is very true about your body. Your body and the extraordinarily large population of microorganisms living there remember how your mind makes them feel.

One study has concentrated on the effects of exercise or meditation on people's health during the cold season. Participants were separated into three study groups.

One was a control group. Another group exercised physically for three weeks and the last group meditated for three weeks. This was done at the beginning of cold season. After this time, the subjects were left to themselves.

In the spring it was evaluated how much, if at all, doing nothing, exercising or meditating had on subjects getting colds. The control group had the most colds. The group who exercised was twice as likely to make it through the whole season without getting a cold. The results of the group who meditated stunned me. They were six times healthier than the control group! Imagine the results of a fourth group that would meditate, exercise and eat nutritious meals.

The effects of regular meditation lasts a long time after the meditation is over. Once you start meditating, it is very easy to do any time you need it.

By this point you can be reading this and saying, "Yeah, one of these books. I am not the meditating type. My mind goes millions miles an hour." Let me assure you. You are not only the perfect type, you need it more than you think.

I had a problem in learning how to meditate. For years. Meditation therapy was actually prescribed for me by a physician in the fifth grade after my liver went crazy. It didn't help. I wasn't able to meditate. Nor when it was suggested again when I was a junior in high school.

I spent six solid months trying to meditate effectively when I was in my early thirties. Two things happened. One was a meeting with a friend who could meditate almost anywhere and in any circumstances.

That gave me a huge confirmation that I could do it, too. She wasn't extraordinary; she knew how to meditate. The second thing that happened was finding a meditation guide online. I liked her voice. She was the first one who made me feel good about my drifting attention and that it was normal.

She suggested imagining my thoughts as clouds that flew by. Every time I got caught in one of those clouds, as soon as I realized that, I let that cloud go. I returned to focusing on my breathing or my heartbeat, knowing that any of these clouds were waiting for me at the end. I no longer felt that I couldn't meditate, so I started. I still meditate almost daily and my attention often drifts for a moment before I let the clouds drift away. I'm far from perfect and that's okay. I benefit highly from meditation.

The most important part of this meditative state is the feeling of love and truth. Your body is never at fault for whatever may be going on with it. Feelings of inner love and forgiveness are essential. You must express truth to your body, in every aspect.

Affirmations help with the process of mediation and will be discussed in the next chapter. They won't work if you don't truly believe what are you saying.

When you start treating your body with genuine unconditional love, your body will start whispering to you about what is best for it. When you are able to connect with your body through meditation, you can feel oncoming health issues right from the beginning.

For example, if you are in tune with your body and catch a cold virus, you will feel that your body is getting ready to eliminate this problem within hours. Normally it takes two to three days before the symptoms of the cold virus manifest. The virus makes sure to breed first, before you can engage help. If you know there is a virus inside you within a couple of hours of catching it, you can effectively consume vitamin C, some sauerkraut or whatever your body needs to support your immune system.

Before Feasts

Life goes on regardless of your best intentions to eat well. Sometimes the opportunity is just too inviting to hold onto your goal. It's okay as long as you don't give up on yourself. It is crucial that you distinguish your body cravings from your mind cravings. For example, sugar as an addictive drug, is almost always a mind craving. Unless you have a condition where sugar is saving you from acute health failure. Binge eating is another example of mind craving. Your body isn't hungry when you are vacuuming the refrigerator at midnight. Pay attention to these.

Write down the occasions where you are aware of your mind cravings and when you actually feel the cravings of your body. You shouldn't have any problem recognizing them. Your body craves what is best for it. Your body doesn't crave anything that can hurt it unless you are starving and your body needs calories in any form.

It may seem silly to keep it written down, but it is actually a very powerful tool to see the date and time you felt this way on paper. You can also come to a conclusion about what triggers your mind cravings.

There are occasions when there is an opportunity to eat new and exciting meals--a wedding or a luxury cruise. I believe that you should take the opportunity to truly enjoy eating the food that is new or eyecatching. Do it and savor every bite. But before you indulge into eating a six-course Valentine's dinner or go to a family reunion, meditate about it. Take time to let your body know first. Tell it that you are going to eat food that you don't wish your body will store as fat or that the food may not be as clean as it needs to be. Ask your body during meditation to push it through your GI tract without utilizing more than is needed for your energy that day.

Let your body know that you aren't planning on doing this for a long time. This is the time when you ask favors from your body. When you state that you will do your best to help clean up this mess when the party's over. This means that you are going to be ready to eat well and supply foods that pull toxins out or go on a short detox diet for couple of days. Then make sure that you keep that promise and thank your body.

I remember going on ten-day cruise and asking my body ahead of time to handle the load of over-stuffing myself. I admit that for a person who eats simply and repeats the same foods, when I saw the food that was calling to be eaten, I wanted it. I was the person at the table with no shame in ordering six different main meals and all the desserts on the menu. I ate more than I saw anyone eat. Yet when I got home, I had gained nothing. Cruise lines have researched how much people gain while on board--almost two pounds per day!

Try to keep in mind avoiding food that contains GMO ingredients in any form. Like corn syrup or enchiladas in corn tortillas. Enjoy the food even if it isn't the best for you. Because your love and acceptance of yourself is going to make sure that you stay on your path, even if you take an occasional detour.

A Daily Meditation

Every morning when I wake up I spend a moment to acknowledge my body. First, I lay on my back with my hands along my sides. I close my eyes or don't open them from sleep and bring my consciousness into my body.

First I feel my feet and send them love and care. I express thanks for the fact that my feet have to carry my whole body all day long.

Then I scan my legs slowly up from my feet. I try to feel them inch-by-inch. I send loving energy continually.

I move my awareness up my arms with love and joy every time I wake up. I feel the palms of my hands. I wiggle my fingers a little and concentrate on them. I have a neurological condition that causes me to wake up sometimes without any sensation in my fingers or even whole arms some days. This leaves soon after I am awake, but my hands used to be weak and small motor movements such as handwriting used to be a challenge. So I do spend a bit longer sending my consciousness there.

When I reach the torso of my body I cruise through the organs. I take a moment to imagine my organs inside and feel them. I feel the air coming and exiting my lungs. I send some love to my liver, stomach, etc.

And at last I feel my heart. I imagine the amazing pump that is making my life possible. In the final moments, I feel my head. I feel my face and open my eyes.

After this, I look at my dog. She is always ready to come and offers me her fur to feel between my fingers. We both exchange loving energy. My hands and fingers are ready to work after petting my dog. It's a great reward for the start of my day.

This whole meditation is very short. It's more of an awareness moment than deep meditation and much shorter than my evening meditation. This takes just a minute or two. You don't need to get up any earlier to do this. That moment spent meditating is often just the moment we are trying to convince ourselves to get up. This can give you energy to move through your morning faster.

The point is to bring awareness into your body as the first thing you do everyday. To be the good farmer who gets up in the morning and takes care of his livestock before he goes inside and has breakfast. Let your body know that you love it and that you wish to be aware of what is going on inside.

Meditation in the morning is pretty easy because your mind and body are already calm from sleep. This is very good for a beginner. If your thoughts start to be distracted by events to come, just simply tell yourself to keep them for after the meditation. Consciously tell yourself that you aren't disregarding your thought processes, they only need to wait. You know what? They will.

After mediation, your mind will restart your thoughts. Just don't fall back asleep.

Another great thing about focusing your awareness inside your body in the morning is that you have an empty stomach. Unless the situation requires it, I would never recommend meditating on a full stomach. Your body is simply busy working and doesn't have a time for discussion.

There are many different techniques of meditation. Some are done sitting down, some lying down. Some you do with your eyes closed and some with eyes open. Although I have the highest respect for the way Tibetan Buddhists meditate, which is sitting down with eyes open and being aware of everything around you, for the purpose of being connected with your body I recommend these meditations be done with your eyes closed. Lying down can be easier for a novice however sitting is just as effective.

It may seem like a good idea to dive into meditating and get a better body as fast as you can. But this isn't a sprint. It's a marathon. Don't try to meditate longer than it feels comfortable. In the beginning, meditate for one minute if you are new to meditation or a chronic beginner.

If you still have a problem focusing inward for one minute, then focus only on your breath. Feel your stomach rising with each inhalation. Imagine your bright pink lungs filling with air. Set your timer for one minute and do that. If you are using an alarm clock to wake you up, set the snooze button to one minute.

I know setting a timer seems a little unromantic, but it works. Once you master one minute, add one more. If you do this every day when you wake up, you will feel a difference in your body and your health within three to four weeks. Send love to yourself and your body for the first minute of your awakened day and watch miracles happen.

I do a second meditation in the evening. I have to be a bit honest and say that at this point of my life I do the evening check-ins less often. During the process of tuning in, it is a very important meditation because it gives you the chance to reflect on yourself. Not your body, but you.

During the morning meditation you are checking how the body feels. Evening meditation places your mind inside your body, a way to be honest about how you treated your body during the day. It's your chance to apologize to your body or have it praise you. It is a vital moment of reflection. I do this every time I know I messed up and also when I feel I did really great. Getting your body's praise feels heavenly. It's like getting an A+ on a subject you were failing so long.

Evening meditation generally takes longer. It is also harder to navigate. Yet this is the time when the magic happens. Give thanks to your body. Especially give thanks to the parts of your body that have problems.

Give thanks to your feet for carrying you, your heart for pumping all the blood and your lungs for bringing in the extra oxygen.

If you have a health issue in some part of your body, give thanks to that part for working the best as it can under the circumstances. The parts of your body that are suffering need more love because the chances are that they are more abused, yet they are still trying to do their best.

Get yourself a notebook and after meditation write about how it made you feel. Did you have a new sensation, feel a stronger connection to your body? Were you too distracted by your thoughts? Keep a record. The more you document this, the easier it becomes to feel more. You can hear your body whisper stronger during this time. The more you write down your thoughts, the more you can understand your body. It's like writing down dreams. If you constantly write them down in the morning, the more you will remember.

As my thanks to you for buying this book, I am giving you a free download of a longer meditation to do in the evening at https://otakaraklettke.com/meditation

Record it with your own voice, adjust it to your needs and play it for yourself.

In this chapter you learned about the importance of meditation. It is the most important key to be able to communicate with your body.

In the next chapter you will learn about affirmations, when and how to use them for your benefit and which kind of affirmations do not help you.

Chapter 11

Affirmations

*"Affirmations are our mental vitamins, providing
the supplementary positive thoughts we need to balance
the barrage of negative events and thoughts
we experience daily."*

Tia Walker

In this chapter you are going to look at affirmations and how to communicate with your body when you are expecting to deal with something unusual.

An affirmation is an act in which we confirm something to be true.

Affirmations can be very good tools when used properly. During an affirmation you consciously tell yourself something in a normal state of mind. You don't need to decrease the frequency of your brain waves. You can use it at any point of the day.

Research proves that meditation really works.

Affirmations have dual results. Sometimes they help and sometimes they actually promote self-doubt and worsen the condition the person was hoping to better.

How shall we make sure that affirmations help? It must be a true statement at all times. If you are saying something that you wish to be true, but in your heart you don't believe it, you are lying to yourself. True self-love can be possible only when you embrace everything about yourself. You don't need to like everything; you only need to be honest and true without self-judgment.

You don't want to say anything to yourself that isn't true. For example, "I am in great shape. I love to eat healthy foods and exercise daily. Every day my body is thinner and thinner. Losing pounds is easy for me." You get the picture. Of course, you can tell yourself this when it's true. But if you spend years trying different diets, hate exercising, and every pound you lose is like trying to remove chewing gum from your hair, you're in trouble.

An affirmation would be more effective if it sounded something like this: "I am learning to accept my body and its shape. I desire to love every part of me at all times. I am learning how to change my diet. I enjoy dancing as a form of exercise. I know when I dance, my soul comes alive and my body gets much needed movement. I celebrate every pound that I lose."

Do you see the difference?

Like your meditations, you can record affirmations in your own voice and listen to them. It is better if you learn them by heart so you can repeat them to yourself whenever you need them. The best and the most exact affirmation is the one you create for yourself.

Creating affirmations is also a great exercise for your mind. Actively trying to create true and positive statements about your body helps to change the overall dialog you have with yourself. You create new pathways for the neurons to fire and lock in new ways of communication.

Affirmations don't have to be long. Use a single sentence like "I desire to do this" or several affirmations that last a few minutes. You can also create statements you need right on the spot.

In this chapter we have looked at affirmations. When they work and when they don't. Now you have the tools needed to create your own effective affirmations.

In the next chapter I am going to talk about exercise and how to stick to it. Even if you are a person who doesn't like the idea of tormenting your body at the gym, you can find movement that will resonate so you can be happy and encouraged not to quit.

Chapter 12

Exercise

*"Motivation is what gets you started.
Habit is what keeps you going."*

Jim Ryun

There are three types of people when it comes to exercise. The first are those who think regular exercise is easy. They perform their sports religiously and it actually bugs them to take a day off. The second type of person has a very hard time getting motivated to start and even if they start, they just can't sustain the program. The third type is a mix. They start, keep going, often for a year or more and then stop for a year or more. If given the chance, they start again.

I am the third type. I don't think that I am an exercise addict. However, I do enjoy it for the most part as well as the benefits that come with it. I can get lazy and stop for a while or longer.

When my daughter was born I took a four-year break from exercising. It was more exhausting to nurse and run after a toddler than any workout.

While pregnant, my dog walked me ten miles daily. I think he was mad that I was pregnant because he never did such a thing before. That's why I don't say that I was walking him. He insisted on those miles. But as soon as my baby was born, all the exercise stopped.

You have probably found yourself in one of the three groups listed above. If you find yourself in the second group and can't get motivated or keep exercising, it doesn't mean that you are set in that group forever. Find an exercise that is right for you.

People often think that to get in shape they have to go to a gym. As a former personal trainer I have encountered many people who take that road. I think it's a great idea when going to the gym is the thing for you. But often it isn't. And if it isn't, you may get discouraged from finding the right exercise.

I had clients who quit within the first five sessions and clients who came obese and devoted themselves to exercise fully while battling binge eating later on in the day. In my personal experience, I have found that binge eaters do well working out and sustaining an exercise program if they aren't ashamed of their bodies. Later on I'll explain why.

You can be the person who has no problem exercising regularly. In order to do that, two things need to happen. Interestingly, it isn't time limitations that stop you from exercising. If you want to find time to exercise, you will find time for it. It's that simple.

The first thing you need to do is to find a type of exercise that makes you happy. If I were to put myself on a basketball team, I would hate every minute of it. If you are a team player in other aspects of your life, a team sport may be the best choice for you.

Dancing is another form of exercise that you can do, even at home. You don't have to join a Zumba class. Although taking your partner and signing up for ballroom dancing can make you feel like a king and queen and spark some late night exercise.

You can play your own favorite music and dance in the way that makes your heart smile. I know that dance is in every one of us. I know people are taught by their environment to be shameful of their body movements. If you feel that way, don't worry. Dance at home to what you like and how you like it. You don't need to try to burn a certain amount of calories or exercise certain muscles. If dance can bring you joy, do it.

I love to watch people dance, I love to watch professional performances. But the true joy is watching people who dance with their hearts and let music move their bodies. The difference is a movement that comes from pure joy.

Dancing became the exercise of my choice in my teen years. It didn't improve my health. But it wasn't the cause of any of my acute problems either. I could dance small amounts of time when I wasn't ill. So I did. Given limited time, I worked hard on my splits and turns and tap dancing since I was the only one in the group who didn't begin at the tender age of five or six. I was fourteen.

Dancing brought happiness to my heart. I didn't fear that my team would fail because of me. I felt free during dancing. I could stretch without losing my breath. There was enough joy that I trained my lungs to handle more and more. I had to be very careful about eating due to my liver, but I learned what my body needed and was able to time it so I wouldn't face the consequences. I wasn't able to ask my body to heal itself yet, but I was able to listen to it enough to have some fun.

Going to a gym is a good way to exercise. If you haven't ever done that, I would strongly suggest you choose a really good workout partner or a trainer. Having accountability to a partner is close to a must if exercising is new to you.

As I mentioned earlier, I have worked with a few people who had binge-eating problems. When they were okay with being seen at the gym regardless of their physical appearance, they were very devoted to working out.

Binge eating is an addiction in which the person is self-harming and knows it. That can be broken easier by replacing the habit with something that would feel similar. It's a bad habit replaced by a good habit with a very different outcome.

For some of you, sex is the best form of exercise. It boosts your immune system more than anything else. Men burn twice as many calories than women on the average. Sex isn't an exercise that burns as many calories as you would wish. Women have more receptors to feel more pleasure from sex. It's a great way to connect to your mind, soul and body. Bringing yourself inside your body and concentrating on the experience from a meditative inner state can bring women an amazing experience that resonates for a long time and can be the best experience for her partner.

Women can even pass out from a good orgasm. Good sex flushes your body with hormones and makes your brain create pleasure drugs that give you healing powers. It temporarily turns your body into a selfhealing machine.

From an evolutionary standpoint, this makes sense. If you are procreating, you need to stay alive. You are doing what your genetic code is pre-programmed to do. We get a huge dose of dopamine and that is a good replacement for binge eaters.

Another form of exercise can be a calm walk with your pet or spouse. It helps with the body as well as the mind.

If you have mobility or extreme overweight issues, you can swim.

There is always something that can make you happy. Movement gives us joy. Find out what gives you joy. Dig into the favorite activity of your childhood and return to it.

I picked up Taekwondo at the age of thirty-eight when my daughter started. She was the only girl among boys. I didn't care about the fact that the next-oldest person in the class was half my age. I cared about the martial art itself. It made me happy to do this, especially with my daughter.

There is no box you have to fit in. There is also no need to think outside of a box that doesn't exist. The only limitation is in your mind.

I would like to remind you that it is a good idea to consult with a good doctor about your plan if your health requires it. I did all I did without a doctor and actually more against a doctor's orders. It worked for me, but I am not you or know your individual body.

Above all, have someone to exercise with you. Having a partner makes things much easier. Or take a course and have a teacher. Everything is easier if you aren't alone. Even if your partner is your little child or a dog and you have to do it at home, do it together. Take your baby on a stroller walk.

Run with your dog.

After you know what makes you happy, go for it. This will give you momentum. You need momentum to build a habit. Whatever you chose to do will work best if you do it daily and at the same time. Choose something that takes less time and do it every day at that time rather than choosing a hard workout two times per week. If you join some course, choose something at least three times per week and if you can, add some kind of movement on your days off.

Science says that it takes three to six weeks to build a habit. Keep that in mind. When you have no idea how long it is going to take, you are more likely to give up. When you know that in three weeks you will have no problem getting up twenty minutes earlier to take your dog on a longer walk, you can make it.

The first week or two, you run on the momentum from the excitement. Then you may have a few tough days. Cross off each day on your calendar if need be and keep track until you succeed in achieving the three-week marker. Even if the habit isn't fully set, you should no longer mind doing the exercise.

When you start doing something you really enjoy, you are on your way to building a habit in only three weeks. This means that you will get up and you and your dog will be very happy to go outside and welcome a new day. You would actually miss it if you didn't do it.

I like to do a small stretching exercise in the morning. I recommend stretching even if you exercise at another time of day. It wakes up your farm and gets you ready to function.

I personally do a quick routine of five Tibetan rites. It is a series of exercises that are at least 2500 years old. It is said that these are rejuvenating exercises and many books have been written about how even old people who start late in life lose their canes and start to grow hair with color instead of gray.

These exercises are your fountain of youth. It takes me less than five minutes to do the exercises and gives me energy for hours. Popular exercises have come and gone and nobody can hold a patent on this ancient form of keeping young. You can find these rites online should you wish to check it out.

After reading this chapter I hope that you know what will be your next form of exercise. You also know that in order for it to become easy, you need to turn it into a habit that takes three to six weeks to form. After this time your routine becomes habitual.

In the next chapter we will look at water, the fluid that makes up the biggest part of your body. The importance of water is the difference in its quality.

Chapter 13

Water

"Water is the driving force of all nature."

Leonardo da Vinci

Your body is mostly water. We all know that. Every middle school child knows that. Yet we rarely care about the quality of this fluid.

The best water you can possibly get is the water that comes out of the ground right at your home. If you own a well and your water is tested as safe, drinkable water, congratulations! Drink it, make your drinks, and cook your food with it. Pack it with you when you leave your home and don't buy pre-made drinks. You are "well" set. Skip the next few paragraphs.

The next best thing is well water that needs some tweaking

to be safe to drink. I am impressed by how many amazing devices are on the market that clean water. Even if the well water is not good, it can be filtered without any chemical additives such as chloride or fluoride.

If you are living on city water, you should know how your city water is treated in order to use it safely. In most cases, cities use chemicals to clean the water. It doesn't matter what the results are, you shouldn't put chemically treated water in your body without some kind of filtering system. Thankfully, there are simple filters on the market to help you.

Most drinks we pick up at the gas station or grocery store are made with city water. Be aware of that.

What frightens me the most is not the chemicals that are used to make the water clear from pathogens. These chemicals can be cleared out. The scariest thing about city water is that the estrogen hormone cannot be filtered.

I talked on this subject with Georgi Bidenko, the executive director of their family business, Environment Commerce. It is the only company in the world as I am editing this book that can clean estrogen from water. Sadly, the technology is new and one company can't change the world's water supply in a heartbeat.

The biggest problems are birth control pills. They contain high amounts of estrogen that are released through urine into our sewage systems. Treatment plants clean most sewage water well, except for the hormones. This water then goes into rivers and follows its natural cycle.

Along the way, the estrogen in the water has a huge impact on our rivers. It changes the sex of fish for example. Back in 1999, James J. Nagler of the University of Idaho led research that showed that 84% of the salmon in the Columbia

River that appeared as female carried male genetic markers. A few studies have shown fish undergoing bizarre mutation right behind city sewer treatment plants, Bidenko told me. Not only are the males becoming females, they also keep their original sex as males and become hermaphrodites, an animal bearing both sexes.

Eventually this estrogen-polluted water reaches a dam that provides city water. The cycle repeats. Now the water has added hormones that are affecting human males. This has been happening for few decades now. Scientists are calling it a sperm-count crisis.

This was first studied in 1990 when Danish researchers claimed a fifty-percent decline in male sperm count since 1940. Keep in mind that the birth control pill became widely available during the fifties.

Later in a study conducted from 1989 until 2005, French researchers published and reported in Human Reproduction a decline in sperm count from 73.6m to 49.9m per milliliter. This study monitored 26,600 healthy men. One of the authors, Joëlle Le Moal, said in the magazine, Guardian, "Since male and female gametes (reproductive cells) are the beginning of all human development, it could be a problem for the next generation's health."

It's not just sperm count that matters. Sperm quality is at stake. If you want a healthy body and healthy body for your children who may not be born yet, you need to think about the water you drink and how you use it in preparing food.

Although the transgender issue has not been associated with the estrogen in the water, I suspect that it has something to do with it. Not in all cases of course, but the amount of kids that cannot connect with their natural genders is increasing and that is odd.

Plastic bottles bring their own risks. Huge amounts of toxins are released into water from the plastic. Buying water that is sourced from underground water systems may eliminate your risk of estrogen, but there may be added phthalates, BPA (chemicals associated with brain damage as well as many other health issues) and at least a dozen more chemical compounds in the plastic bottle itself. The release of the toxins is dependant on how the bottle is handled, how long the water is inside or if the bottle is exposed to direct sunlight.

When you are in a situation where you have to use water bottled in plastic, there are few things you can do to eliminate the risk. Don't expose the bottle to sunlight. Sun breaks down the plastic and causes a release of the chemicals inside it. Don't freeze or microwave the water bottle because the plastic molecules enter the water in high amounts. Don't ever reuse a plastic bottle. Single-use plastic has different safety standards than plastic bottles intended for reuse.

The next best thing to well water is to buy a big container and find a friend or a place where you can get well water and bring it home. Artesian spring water is of course a great solution as well.

Plastic water containers that are meant for repeated use are a bit safer as far as plastic goes. If you get your own water, you need to be aware of how long the water remains in plastic. You can transfer the water into a glass or metal container at home.

I keep hearing over and over that we're supposed to drink water in its pure form. I do agree. I also agree that some-times it's not as tasty as flavored drinks. If you have to force yourself to drink water, you simply won't get as much fluid unless you drink something you love. Of course, I don't recommend that your drink of choice contain sugar. Your own body won't recommend that. If your choice of getting a lot of fluid is to drink tea or enhance your water with slices of fruit, go for it.

Listen to your body. It has the right answer. And stay hydrated!

This chapter reminds you of the importance of water, the quality of water and the dangerous levels of hormones that affect water in today's world.

In the next chapter I am going to take you to my favorite place. Outside. I am going to talk about the benefits of being outdoors. You will learn an amazing and free trick that has saved my arm from being numb. You are also going to see how much stress you can reduce by connecting with nature even for a brief moment.

Chapter 14

Outdoors

"Be healthy by being outdoors in the natural daylight with nature!"

Steven Magee

Spending time outdoors is especially important. You are a part of this beautiful planet. Connecting with your body is connecting with nature. The more time you spend outside and the deeper into nature you go, the more you are affected by it. It slows you down, unless you are judging the distance between you and a wild bear.

The frequency that nature operates on is different than most of your busy life. When you spend time in nature, you slowly get saturated with that frequency. If you spend a week or more camping in the wilderness, you know how hard it feels to return to a busy life. If you ever talk to someone who has hiked on a long journey for months, he would tell you that returning to civilization is a scary and almost surreal moment. The deeper I travel into virgin land, the more I feel soaked by this energy. This is the frequency that your body operates on. During meditation in nature, you can sit with your farm in peace while discussing how to turn your body into a masterpiece.

The side effects of calming your mind are the feelings of joy and peace. Nature is a great antidepressant. Studies show that planting more trees in the city reduces the overall mental problems of its citizens.

Students allowed to walk in the park for thirty minutes before taking a test, performed significantly better than students who didn't. Just a city park!

I believe you owe it to yourself to spend a few days at least once a year in a true natural area that hasn't been groomed by human beings too much.

There is also the obvious benefit of fresh air. Air in the forest is filled with essential oils and phytoncides. Phytoncides are volatile organic compounds emitted by trees and plants. They prevent the growth of attacking organisms. Air near water is filled with negative ions that are natural antidepressants. Take your next hike near some river.

Do I need to mention that trees clean the air and provide fresh oxygen that we cannot survive without? I am sure you know that. Keep it in mind.

Time spent outdoors will also allow the micro-helpers on your skin to turn sunshine into vitamin D that is needed for absorbing calcium.

There is one more gem that being outside offers, even on your front porch.

Grounding or Earthing

Grounding for a human being means the same as it means for grounding a house. It is connecting electrically with the Earth.

Humans have lived forever walking barefoot and connecting every step with Earth. You have electricity in your body. Some you generate on your own. With every thought and even at this moment when reading this book, you are creating electrical impulses. Some electricity you absorb from your modern lifestyle. Walking barefoot or even during gardening, you connect with Earth and release your excess electricity.

Unfortunately, western civilization created shoes with rubber soles that do not allow you to ground while being outside. Gardening seems like a hobby saved for the retired.

Earth is a giant reservoir of negatively charged free electrons. You carry positively charged electrons. The lives of human beings are filled with their computers, cell phones and televisions. Houses are one giant net full of radio signals, Wi-Fi, Bluetooth and microwaves, just to name the few. We are constantly getting loaded with the positive charge that causes our blood cells to coagulate.

What happens during grounding is that we release this positive charge into the ground and our blood cells let go of each other. It doesn't take long. You can have your blood drawn before and after thirty minutes of grounding and see it yourself under the microscope.

A friend told me about grounding. I was dealing with a weird thing happening to my hands and arms. One day I woke up and I didn't feel my hand. I got super scared. Even though my hand soon started having some tingling sensations and returned to normal, I remained worried. This happened when I was in my late twenties and continued to get worse for a decade.

My doctor thought it was my nervous system and suggested massages. That didn't help. I asked natural healers. They all had their points of view, but nothing helped. I got worse. I still regained sense in my arm every morning, but my fine motor skills suffered. I couldn't draw pictures with my daughter. I could only write for a very limited time. Using silverware was a challenge on the harder days.

When my daughter turned five, I remember going to the passport office to renew her passport. I couldn't fill in the form. I couldn't write or even sign my name. Tears filled my eyes in that office and I realized I had to find real solution.

When my hands had no feeling I couldn't 'talk' to them. I was physically quite fit and most of my health issues were already gone. The problem with my hands was something I was unable to address.

When my friend told me about grounding, my world changed. I got up every day and went outside, sat down on the ground and buried my hands and bare feet in the dirt. From the very first day, my condition started improving. No doctors, no massages, no herbal supplements, nothing that cost me a dime. After a decade of despair, I started to write and started to feel my hands again.

When I woke up with pain in my hands. I cannot tell you how excited I was to have the pain instead of feeling nothing. As I grow older I try to feel grateful for pain, as it is my body's way of pointing out things I need to pay attention to. Thankfully,

I haven't had to deal with severe pain for years. You should always ask a doctor for evaluation when dealing with serious issues.

Make a point of walking barefoot from spring to fall outside as much as possible. If you can't do that, at least stand outdoors barefoot. Just two years ago it would have been impossible for me to write this book. In winter I seem to maintain the grounding influence without going barefoot. Occasionally, I wake up with lost sensation or pain in my fingers or hand. Thankfully I know what to do.

Nature is a beautiful place to heal mind, body and soul. It is also a place to ground yourself by releasing positively charged electrons into negatively charged Earth.

In the next chapter you will learn about supplements.

I am not going to recommend that you take anything. Rather I will show you some alarming facts about what you can buy on the market and the regulations that are needed for vitamins and other supplements.

You don't want to miss this one.

Chapter 15

Vitamins and Other Micronutrients

"Good nutrition and vitamins do not directly cure disease, the body does. You provide the raw materials and the inborn wisdom of your body makes the repairs. Someday healthcare without megavitamin therapy will be seen as we today see childbirth without sanitation or surgery without anesthetic."

Andrew W. Saul

It is common knowledge that you need micronutrients in order to function properly. What is not common knowledge is that you can get all you need from your diet. Harvard Medical School published an article in their magazine about the longterm effects of multivitamin pills. There really wasn't much of an effect--only a small decrease in cancer.

Vitamins are organic compounds that the human body needs

and cannot create itself. Animals, too, need vitamins and they are commonly different for them than for us. You need very little of these compounds, but they are essential to your body's development. Now it is very important to understand how individual your body is. Everyone, depending on lifestyle, has different vitamin needs.

You should get vitamins from your food or sunshine in case of vitamin D. Learn what you need most, based on your lifestyle and simply search for a list of foods that are abundant in that vitamin. Regularly eat the ones that sound the best.

To be fully clear, your body can create some vitamins out of provitamins. For example, beta carotene, found in carrots and other vegetables is a provitamin and your microorganisms turn it into vitamin A.

When it comes to adding vitamins and other micronutrients in the form of a pill or any form that you purchase in the store, I am quite skeptical. And you should be too. Here's why.

The regulation of dietary supplements varies from country to country. In the United States, vitamins and other supplements fall under the Dietary Supplement Health and Education Act of 1994. The Food and Drug Administration is subordinate to this Act and cannot require more stringent regulation to any supplement.

This act is wildly confusing. It hardly regulates anything. It basically allows any manufacturer to market any supplement that existed before 1994 without FDA approval. Supplements that have seen the light of day after 1994 are defined as new dietary ingredients and based on the FDA Draft Guidance on New Dietary Ingredients for the Dietary Supplement Industry. They must "provide reasonable evidence of their safety, or reasonable expectations of their safety."

FDA approval lawyer, Susan Frank, told me exclusively for this book: "FDA approval is not required for any finished Dietary Supplement product regardless of when the product was first on the market. However, a manufacturer must submit a premarket notification for any new ingredient that was not previously used in food."

She went on to explain that under the DS Act, companies are prohibited from putting a product on the market that is adulterated or misbranded.

Susan says: "DS manufactured in dirty conditions, or with foreign-sourced ingredients would be examples of adulterated products.

Many raw ingredients are foreign-sourced. For example, ginger, a common DS ingredient, may come from a distributor in India who sourced the ingredient from China. The manufacture of the finished product may not have actual control or knowledge as to the conditions under which the raw ingredient was manufactured. This can be a problem.

Misbranded refers to labeling. The labeling must be truthful and not misleading. For ingredients that are naturally sourced, the FDA cannot require the amount stated on the label be exact because of the large variation that can occur in naturally sourced ingredients.

Because DS cannot make drug claims, e.g. treat or cure, a DS is not evaluated for effectiveness. Even though these manufacturers cannot make drug claims, sometimes the way a product is packaged or labeled makes it seems like a drug. Claims about a product supporting or promoting a health condition, may sound like a drug claim to a consumer. The consumer may believe that they are getting a product that has been evaluated for effectiveness."

I personally don't trust a lot of products on the market. I trust the ones that are from a reliable manufacturer and usually contain one or very few ingredients. I have no trust in popular 'healthy' shakes containing a long list of ingredients that were sourced from all over the world.

As this book is being finished, the New York State Attorney General's office finished investigating instore brands of herbal supplements in Walmart, Walgreens, Target and GNC. These businesses were taking full advantage of the regulation that doesn't protect the consumer.

For example, none of the store brands selling Gingko Biloba contained that medicinal plant, even though it was labeled as such. Other supplements don't have any trace of the ingredients on their labels and some have only traces of the DNA of the product.

All companies received cease and desist letters ordering them to stop selling these supplements. This information was published in New York Times and is available online. It is no wonder that studies don't show the benefits of taking multi-vitamin pills versus not taking them.

A couple of years ago I became a fan of Manuka honey for its advertised, amazing properties. I spent a lot of money on this overpriced product. I haven't found it any more effective than the honey I buy from a local beekeeper. Later I read an article about New Zealand, the only place this particular honey comes from. The manufacturers exported more Manuka honey than they had produced. Some of this honey was fake. I raise my own bees now.

When it comes to buying supplements I would suggest you exercise extreme caution. If you don't know the company personally, you have little assurance of the quality of the product.

Some manufacturers actually do undertake clinical trials in order to have proof for advertising claims they make. You can search on www.clinicaltrials.gov for a product or ingredient to find clinical trials of a DS manufacturer.

Some supplements, including vitamins, are volatile. For example, cooking destroys vitamin C. Do you also know that exposure to air and light destroy this vitamin as well?

Famous eccentric billionaire Howard Hughes believed in the power of fresh-squeezed orange juice. He had oranges squeezed in front of him right before he consumed the juice. Today, we know he was right.

How much you cut up a fruit or vegetable can play a role in vitamin loss. Juice that sits in a clear bottle on a lighted store shelf won't necessarily contain the amount of vitamins advertised on the bottle. The good news is that with a little bit of education, you can get what you need in your diet naturally. And your body knows how to extract micronutrients from food much easier than it does from a pill.

I should note that it is very hard to get enough calcium and vitamin D through food. Especially women need a lot of calcium and the demand increases with age. Vitamin D is often neglected with the lack of exposure to sunlight. In cloudy cities and in jobs that don't allow people to spend time outdoors, getting enough vitamin D and calcium can be challenging, although not impossible. For example, you can use grow lights instead of regular lights that have the same spectrum as the sun and provide you with vitamin D.

Be smart about your choices. You don't need to waste money on placebo pills and you shouldn't trust a source unless you know it. Investigate the company. You can make your own supplements. I was raised on a homemade calcium supplements and cough syrups. Picking wild medicinal herbs was the first money I ever made in middle school.

Eat fruit that has had a chance to ripen on the tree. Consume foods that don't have to travel long distances to reach you. Keep your diet simple, yet full of nutritious food. Grow food or have chickens provide eggs. At least buy what you can from your farmer's market or barter food with friends.

Instead of a grassy lawn, let nature bring wild plants to your yard. You never know when you can save yourself or a family member with something wild that grows near your doorstep. Use a simple Internet search to learn about the specific plants around you.

In this chapter I discussed dietary supplements. Also that the regulation of supplements isn't strict and it's hard to trust in many circumstances. If you are curious about clinical trials of certain products, research www.clinicaltrials.gov.

In the next chapter, I will talk about weight control and how to get rid of excess weight, or to be clear, excess body fat. Your body wants to be healthy. It also wants to have an appropriate shape. How to achieve that will be the next hot topic.

Chapter 16

Weight Gain, Weight Loss

"While weight loss is important, what's more important is the quality of food you put in your body - food is information that quickly changes your metabolism and genes."

Mark Hyman

I would like to dedicate this chapter to all of you who feel the need for adjusting your body weight. As with anything that affects your body, please be smart.

Weight Gain

Changing body weight can be a frustrating process. As a toddler and child I was underweight. From what I've learned, it seems harder to gain weight for those who are naturally slender than to lose it.

To add insult, the majority of the population that needs to lose weight slanders slender people.

Not being able to gain weight can be a signal that something is not right in your body. Not always. Some people have a metabolism that is able to handle almost anything thrown at it. These people have a good working farm and I am quite sure they don't regularly dine in fast food restaurants.

Not being able to gain good, quality weight--muscle instead of fat, can be a sign of a high level of stress. In this case, it's good to get a basic blood test to be sure there is nothing to address.

There are a few things that you can do about weight gain.

Eat more often. A small body gets full faster. Adding a meal per day to your diet can help increase your caloric intake. Cannabis is a great help for creating appetite. That said, as I mentioned in the Chapter Five, make sure that you are following the laws of your country and state.

Be aware about eating nutritious food. The need to gain weight should not be an excuse to eat low-grade food. Eat meals high in good-quality starch and protein at the same time, like a good bean and bacon soup. As with any other health concern, try to find meals that you love that have a few good ingredients. Stick with these meals. In time you should see results.

If you don't see results and are really healthy, you are just meant to have a small body frame. Don't feel bad. The best news is that your life expectancy is much higher than that of a heavier population.

Weight Loss

While there are many detailed reasons people gain too much

weight, it often comes down to one emotion, fear. Fear causes stress that manifests itself in overeating or undereating which damages organs. You can gain weight even if you are really good about your meals.

True unconditional love of your body is a must if you want to achieve the body that is happy. A happy body isn't overweight or at least not more than few pounds.

I know people who are obese and play the public role of owning up to their big body and shedding humor along the way. All that humor is a way to cope with obesity and public reaction to it.

I am not here to shame you and I am not here to shame your body in any way. I am sure you feel these emotions all by yourself. I did when I hit my teen years and started adding pounds.

I am here to tell you that your soul was given a perfectly amazing body. You can lose a significant amount of weight, if you want to and are willing to help your body to get rid of toxins.

Trust me on that. No heart wants to grow four times its size to keep pumping blood. None of your farm creatures want to work overtime. Your lungs don't want to be short of oxygen. It is your body's nature to return to its comfortable state--not too thin and not too heavy.

You may disagree and tell me that you have health problems and are storing up tires of fat around your bones. You might argue with your last breath about the imperfections of your body.

That doesn't make you unique. Loving your body will. Nobody is perfect. No body. I can waste energy finding so many flaws with my body that they would fill this book. Why would I do that? I don't cover up my flaws.

I love my body as it is.

The best way to start loving your body is to be honest and apologize to it. Do it when you are alone. You can do it in bed while meditating or you can undress and say it to the naked image in your mirror. Your body has never, ever given up on you. Even if you had a near death experience, you are reading this book now.

You have a live body. Can you say to yourself that you have never given up on your body? Remember, your body is protecting you with that fat from toxins. Whatever method you use to apologize to your body, do it when you know you can mean it with all of your spiritual heart.

Your body isn't you. You don't even own it. Yes, you can harm it or end its life, but that still wouldn't make it yours. I am not talking about your body belonging to God. I don't talk about spirituality in this sense.

Your body isn't really yours because you are sharing it with so many microorganisms that keep you alive. All of you are a team. You are the person in the driver's seat, but without your mini-army, you are dead. Embrace this.

You love your body because it is a vessel that keeps your soul and mind on Earth. Even if you think that your bodiless soul can roam around after death, the truth is that without your body, you will never kiss your love, hug your parent, snuggle your baby or say a word out loud. I believe that because your body is composed of living organisms, you have no right to mistreat it.

Say your apologies out loud. Have a whole monologue if you

wish. And after that, shower yourself with love. Send loving thoughts to your body several times a day. When you pass a mirror, smile at yourself and tell yourself that you have a beautiful smile. Because you do.

And when you feel unable to love your body, ask someone who loves you to help. If you don't have anyone, contact me. I can assure you that I love your body. I find your body fascinating to its last cell. I also love your brain and what it can do. Love yourself without anyone's permission. You are in charge of a wonderful machine that is run by you and so many microbes. I don't know what you do for living, but I doubt you are in charge of over 100 trillion living beings.

You have taste buds that give you great pleasure when you use them. I believe that taste buds are bridges of communication between your brain and your body. Unless these taste buds are hijacked by drugs such as sugar, they can help you in enormous ways. I know this may sound puzzling, but trust me. When you start hearing the whispers of your body, your taste will adjust. I promise I won't make you live on a specific diet. You will do that yourself. Your body wants the best for itself.

I have a neighbor who cooks and bakes with so much heart that I have a hard time resisting her food. She is always willing to share, bless her heart. And I am always willing to eat. These moments of craving more food than I need or starchy, sweet food are rare for me. So why not? Moderation is a key when it comes to sweets.

When that time comes for you, enjoy yourself and eat what you like. Never hide by the refrigerator promising yourself that this is the last bite of ice cream that you are going to eat. If you want ice cream, put the amount you see fit in a beautiful glass, top it with fresh fruit, sit down and devour every bite. Take your time to enjoy food.

Fantasize about that bite before you are going to eat it. This will help you to eat less. If you imagine the food you are about to eat and imagine how every bite tastes and feels in your mouth first, you are likely to eat about 30% less food. This is very different from seeing a food advertisement. That would make you eat about 30% more. Imagine the bite, the taste, and the structure before you eat it. Then enjoy it! Scientists call this habituation. The repeated stimulus lowers your body's response to it. That's why the chocolate cake tastes so much better with the first bite than it does half way through.

A body is not self-destructive without the mind creating the destruction.

How long does it take your body to respond to your plea? It's hard to say. Sometimes it can be in an instant. When that moment strikes, all you have to do is to maintain it. Sometimes it takes time for you to truly accept your body with love and sustain that love.

Should you feel that this is taking too long, go to the diet you used during detox and stay on it longer. Slowly ease out by remembering the rules of detox eating for lunch and dinner and later for dinner alone.

Never eat food that is considered low fat when it shouldn't be. Like yogurt. Yogurt needs fat in order to be a true yogurt. Otherwise, starches take the place of the fat. A lot of starch is never a good idea to consume. High quality fat is really good for you. Sugar and starch are not.

Educate yourself using independent sources. In this day and age of massive communication, you have no excuse for not knowing.

Your body will respond in time and whisper to you. You are going to have the biggest love affair of all time with your mind and body!

In both cases of weight gain or weight loss, it is important to accept your body. You choose how to get the best results that make you happy. And drop sugar in any form.

How do you get rid of allergies, the common cold, or long-term issues? That's in the next chapter.

Chapter 17

Getting healthy

"Poor health is not caused by something you don't have; it's caused by disturbing something that you already have. Healthy is not something that you need to get, it's something you have already if you don't disturb it."

Dean Ornish

Having a healthy body is definitely the goal for all of us. Following everything in this book will improve your health. All the steps described in previous chapters should lead you to success.

A body is healthy when it doesn't suffer from any acute problems or any chronic issues. Being healthy is definitely on a scale. At any moment there are pathogens present in your body. There are viruses and unfriendly bacteria inside you right now.

When you are healthy, your body deals with these issues without you ever noticing. It is almost impossible to be 100% healthy every single moment. That is if you define being healthy as being free of anything that doesn't belong in a perfectly functioning body. Your body is usually working on some improvement. Nobody is 100% perfect.

Being unhealthy is on the scale as well. There is a big difference between someone battling a seasonal cold or allergies versus someone battling a life-threatening disease. This book will help to guide you to push that scale toward the healthy side as much as possible and keep it there.

How did Hippocrates, the 'Father of Western Medicine,' cure people? How did he fire up their self-healing mechanisms almost two-and-a-half millennia ago?

In ancient Greece, Hippocrates started the new science of medicine. Disease was treated before, but he was the first who believed that disease had a natural cause and was not some wrath of God bestowed upon a human being. He was the first person to separate medicine from religion. He argued that disease was a product of environment, diet and living habits!

He also believed that "Nature is the physician of diseases." The Latin term, "Vis medicatrix naturae" came later which translates as, "the healing power of nature." Hippocrates fully believed that a body can and will heal itself if given the right conditions.

Patients walked to his hospital on the island of Kos after seeing the beauty of the building from far. After the patient was admitted to the hospital, the first step was to let the patient fast. This served two purposes; the patient got unhealthy food and wine cleansed from the system and two, Hippocrates believed that: "to eat when you are sick, is to feed your sickness."

Hippocratic medicine was so revolutionary that it didn't focus on giving medication. It focused on helping the body rebalance and cure itself. After fasting, he strongly believed in rest and a healthy diet.

As you can see, I am not offering you anything new. I am crying out loud. The medical system swears on the Hippocratic oath and yet doesn't listen or act upon the teachings. Instead it prescribes medications, as did pre-Hippocratic physicians.

It is amazing that in an age of no telephones, internet and advertising that Hippocrates was more famous and unbelievably successful than any other physician. Considering the fact that in his time there was a strong belief that a body could not be dissected or an autopsy performed, his results were astonishing.

Hippocrates had very limited knowledge of what was actually inside the human body. He lived to be ninety years old, as did the people around him.

Just imagine what we can do with the knowledge available to us today combined with his philosophy.

Fasting is definitely one of the best ways to start and even repeat from time to time. One of the most cited neuroscientists, Mark Mattson, lead the study that shows that your brain will actually grow new brain cells when you fast. Note that in the past, it was believed that you are given a certain amount of brain cells at birth and you only killed them as you aged.

If your health allows it, don't eat for one day. Drink only pure water and then slowly introduce healthy meals. That's what Hippocrates would have prescribed to you.

Hippocrates also kept his patients clean in a sterile environment. His way of curing was gentle and kind to the patients. Lots of rest and clean water or wine along with healthy food was the most common way to heal. He had some revolutionary ways of treating some diseases that, believe or not, are still being used today.

If almost all issues are the result of your mind, can your mind cure them? Yes, it can and faster than healthy eating and exercise. The only problem is that it is much harder to reprogram your mind than it is to change your eating and exercising habits. In the end you need both methods. Healthy food and exercise will also help you reset your mind.

I have cured myself and other people from allergies simply by not believing in an allergy in the first place. This actually didn't dawn on me until I was about twenty years old and dating a guy who was allergic to pollen. He said that he had never been allergic until he was in the army with a buddy who was allergic to pollen and somehow this transferred to him.

It was such an outrageous theory that I became allergic to pollen myself! So I spent three months sneezing at flowers and then I said to myself, "This is no fun. If I can get allergic simply by hearing the story of my boyfriend's army buddy, I can just as easily tell my mind to stop." So I did. And it worked.

Just think about how commercials are placing the thought of allergies in your mind. Or when the weather report talks about allergens in the air. This part is something you have to believe in order to work.

I have a friend and she was terribly allergic to dust, pollen and more. I looked in her eyes and kept repeating to her that she had no allergy. First, as everyone does, she argued that she had it.

It truly blows my mind how much people want to hang onto their health issues.

A couple of days later she confessed to me that in my presence she had no symptoms, but as soon as she was on her own she was reaching for the antihistamines. I told her that my energy cared for her enough that when we were together, she didn't show any symptoms. Even when, bless her heart, she helped me clean my old shed full of hundred-year-old farm supplies. Eventually she believed me fully and dumped all her antihistamines.

Note that I find this effective on most allergies except for food. Those are something else and you should listen to the individual needs of your body.

Acute problems such as seasonal colds can be eliminated right from the start. Keeping your body balanced doesn't mean you have to wear armor. You still are going to get attacked by unfriendly bacteria and viruses. However, being able to talk to your body, you become aware of the symptoms sooner. Sometimes within an hour. At that time the foreign microbes don't have much of a chance to breed. You can send help to your body in the form of rest, vitamins, herbal teas, or whatever works for you.

I personally cure almost all of my problems with propolis, honey, and other bee products. They work for me. Propolis heals me from any form of respiratory issue that my body is prone to catch, usually overnight. If it takes me more than twenty-four hours, I consider the attacking bug strong and go to the kitchen for help. I cruise my hand along the line of herbal and normal teas until I feel a connection with one.

This is somewhat scientific and somewhat intuitive. I have a pretty good knowledge of medicinal herbs from my mother who is a botanist specializing in the field, so perhaps I reach for what I know is good. I also believe that my body creates an intuitive pull to the herb that can help me.

I don't end up having strong symptoms of the sickness. My body slays them at the very beginning when it's easy. When you balance your body with your own self-healing machine, you, too, will be able to pick the right herb or understand that a fifteen minute nap or meditation now will make you more productive.

I have zero success with intuitive healers. I have success with my personal intuitive healing process brought forth by my connection with my body as well as the education of healing possibilities.

I also don't have success with doctors. If I have problems, I consult with my friend who is a veterinarian who understands the mammalian body and the way it functions. I take time to find information on anatomy and see pictures of autopsies. Just like Leonardo da Vinci performed autopsies to understand how to paint and sculpture, I look up the position of my organs and how they look so when I meditate I can understand which area is calling for help.

I do believe that doctors can help you search for the mechanical problems of your body. When you break a bone, go to the doctor, please.

Your body can only give you so much information. It does this in a very tranquil, whispering language. It is up to you to be aware which region of your body is calling out for help.

You also need to understand that chronic problems took years to develop and may take months or years to leave you fully. The good news is that within one month, every kind of chronic problem should show signs of reduction. Chronic problems are also something you are used to living with and they are often used as excuses to the people around us or to obtain attention or pity.

I see this in young mothers with their first child. When my daughter was a baby, I was a very isolated mother. Other mothers talked about the problems their child had and the one mom who had the most problems got the most attention. I didn't care to compete for attention by voicing my child's health issues. I was exhausted from being a mom for a healthy baby. I nursed her for over four years and I was tired. I didn't want her sick.

When she was about four and had the second cold in her life, I drove her to the ocean four hours away. Then I told her that if she wanted to play on the beach the next morning, she needed to ask her body to wake up healthy. Believe it or not, she woke up healthy. Motivation to be and stay healthy works for grown ups, and in my house even better for kids.

Watch yourself. Make sure that you aren't looking for pity. Don't discuss your health as a topic in your conversation with friends who aren't there to address the healing. That's very important. This is something you have to answer for yourself. So be truthful about it. Send love to the weak link whether it is a chronic or acute issue you are dealing with. Want to be healthy? Look forward to doing something that makes your heart glow. Eat simple, sleep enough and love yourself, your body farm, and the people around you.

This chapter addressed the teachings of Hippocrates and his amazing approach to healing the body by fasting, a good diet, clean environment, and rest. It is wise not to neglect the power of your mind when it comes to allergies and other health issues.

Thank you for reading my book. With all my heart let me say goodbye to you in the final chapter.

Chapter 18

Compassion

"I have just three things to teach: simplicity, patience, compassion. These three are your greatest treasures."

Lao Tzu

I hope you enjoyed this book as much as I enjoyed writing it. I would love to hear from you. PLEASE LEAVE A REVIEW for the book.

Feel free to contact me at otakara@hearyourbodywhisper.com

Let me know if and how meditations, affirmations, simplifying your diet and finding fun movement for your body work.

I care about your body. I care about you being healthy. I care about you loving yourself. I care because I am aware of the

149

fact that we are all connected. The more you care about your own being, the more you are supporting a healthier planet. Healthy, functioning people mean a better future for us all, our children and this planet.

Love is the most beautiful feeling there is. Enjoy that feeling as much as you can. We are drawn to love. I am still learning and practicing that skill. I can tell you this much, when you are able to finally feel love towards yourself and your body, you will love others in this new way as well. It will help you identify the relationships you have in your life and see if they are benefiting your life or just taking it from you. Your relationship with your body lets you know the same things--whether you are benefiting your body or making your body fear your mind.

You have learned how important it is to eat food in its basic form. Unaltered. Not with recoded DNA in the lab. You also know that keeping your diet simple has been the key to longevity around the world.

I hope you are making your heart dance with the movement you choose for your body. Whether it is dancing, swimming or something else. I hope that you are sticking with it and making it a habit that you look forward to every day.

We need people who can do that to make this world a better place. How can you say that you care about helping a world when you cannot help yourself?

I hope that you are on your way to letting go of the drugs that affect your body in a negative way, such as sugar, artificial sweeteners or nicotine.

The body that carries your soul and protects your thoughts isn't yours. It belongs to a whole super team of various life forms that live in symbiotic relationship with you. In many ways this helps me to be nice to my body. It is much easier to be kind to others than to yourself. You ought to nurture that kindness with love. It is a foundation block that enables you to love others in the same way.

Society's mindset supports self-doubt. It is considered selfish or vain to love yourself. You will be judged. But you will be judged if you don't love yourself either. You will also be praised and admired. In the end, it all comes down to you.

When someone compliments your body, don't take it as your credit only. You work on it along with many organisms and don't forget that genes played a role in how beautiful your eyes are.

You shouldn't care too much about people who may shame you for your body shape. Love yourself anyway. The relationship between you and your body is uniquely yours. Enjoy it. Let's start a revolution!

Tell yourself often, "I honor, respect and love my body."

About the Author

Otakara Klettke. Nobody would ever guess that this lady who is full of life, adventures, stories from traveling the world, and living in 4 countries, was once a very sickly child that couldn't even carry her school books.

How did she manage to escape special diets, constant visits to a doctor, surgeries, and hospital stays, and was able to become a personal fitness trainer, adventurer, and TV reporter while keeping her body in the same shape once she grew up?

She talks and listens to her body. In her book, Hear Your Body Whisper, she shares how she said "No!" to the limitations of her health problems, left doctors in the dust, and started living life to the fullest.

Currently she lives in the beautiful Cascade mountain range in Oregon, raising too many pets, and taking every chance to go on road trips with her brilliant homeschooled daughter.

Learn more and stay in touch at www.otakaraklettke.com

Made in the USA
Monee, IL
30 August 2020